living life on the veg

✔ KU-821-246

2007
Organic market growth came to an abrupt halt.

2007
Wild garlic provides many years of employment for Watson children, developing strong backs and nimble fingers.

2006
Environmental impact study with Exeter University spelled the end of Riverford sourcing tomatoes, peppers, cucumbers from UK & Dutch heated glass, and the founding of our Spanish grower group.

2005
Samphire discovered on the marshes of a coop member – the first of many years of painstaking picking.

2005
Riverford opened its Field Kitchen restaurant on the farm.

2009
Guy fell in love with cardoons; his mission to convert the nation has so far failed.

2009
Bought farm in the Vendee in France to meet the Hungry Gap challenge. A chance to experiment with a whole range of new crops.

2010
Riverford Travelling Field Kitchen toured the country in a yurt to promote the joys of veg.

2012
Tomatillos grow on the Vendee farm – more readily than our customers consume them.

2018
Riverford becomes 74% employee owned.

2015
Riverford voted The Observer's Ethical Product of the Decade.

2014
Finding loofahs growing rampantly in Spain set Guy on another experimental crop.

2013
Green-fronded Italian agretti is the next veg experiment.

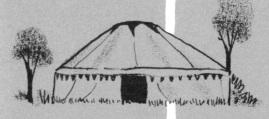

vegetables, soil & hope

To our loyal customers and the critical friends
who keep us honest

vegetables, soil & hope

ruminations of a lifelong veg nerd

GUY SINGH-WATSON

Text © 2018 Riverford Organic Farms Ltd

The right of Riverford Organic Farms Ltd to be identified as the
author of the work has been asserted by them in accordance with
the Copyright, Designs and Patents Act 1988.

First published in 2018

Cataloguing in Publication Data is available from the British Library

ISBN: 978-0-9932155-2-0

Project editor: Anna Neima
Design: Smith & Gilmour
Illustrations: Berger & Wyse. www.bergerandwyse.com
Other illustration: Ariel Cortese at Big Fish

Printed and bound in Italy by L.E.G.O.

www.riverford.co.uk

lexicon
Terms marked with * are possibly unfamiliar to non-farmers
and are explained on pages 188–191

introduction

Since donning my first wellies I have always wanted to be a farmer. My early forays into pigs (my eighth birthday present) and sheep (a teenage enterprise) had mixed success and I was twenty-six when I sowed my first leeks. Looking back over thirty years of growing and cooking vegetables I realise how lucky I am to have found my vegetable calling. To be able to follow that calling with so little compromise, within my own business, with the trust and support of our loyal customers, has given my life a level of autonomy and purpose which is both a privilege and a responsibility. I have never been a follower. Like my parents (first generation, idealistic but impractical farmers), I have spent a lifetime farming and running a business 'my way' with scant regard for convention. Pa had a crazy idea a year (keeping pigs in houses built of straw bales one year, making wind generators from oil drums the next). Most of my schemes fail, as most of his did, but enough have worked to keep us going for a combined sixty-seven years. Veg boxes were one of my better ideas.

Like most introverts I recharge my batteries and think best alone. Ideas are mostly born and shaped when I am on my own: in the fields with my beloved vegetables, on a surfboard waiting for a wave, or in the bath. Quite a few make their way into the weekly newsletters that have accompanied our deliveries of vegetables each week for over twenty-five years. Incubation time is vital; nothing works better for me than repetitive physical work which leaves the mind untethered. After unfettered and frequently circular mental wanderings, I normally find it quite easy to get the ideas onto paper, though it typically takes three goes over three days to shape them into the allotted 380 words by Wednesday morning.

These missives, rants, news pieces are reproduced here pretty much as I wrote them, bar a few references to events with no current relevance. We have lost many of the early ones but looking back I am surprised by the constancy in tone and themes of the ones we have unearthed. My lodestar has remained the pursuit of good farming, good food and good business. Perhaps the biggest changes are a decline in anger (which is a relief), a growing reluctance to be gratuitously offensive (which makes life easier) and a growing tolerance and appreciation of the virtues of looking for solutions rather than problems. On a good day I wonder if I have finally grown up.

I have an anarchic and irreverent streak that makes me question, and often resent, the role of management. Nothing saps my spirit more than a board meeting and nothing invigorates me more than seeing people question management and figure out a better way of doing things for themselves. My father believed that, with the right attitude, his staff could do anything; he was wrong in the detail and failed to help them with much training, direction or structure, but he was right in spirit and his enduring faith in humanity is his most lovable trait. Probably the most frequently recurring theme in this book is a frustration with conventional management and the demeaning assumption that the best, or even the only, way to motivate and organise is through appealing to individual avarice. Given the wealth of evidence that money is a poor and short-lived motivator, the prevalence and persistence of the perception that it the best way of getting things done is extraordinary, frustrating and staggeringly wasteful. Most people are kinder, less greedy, more creative, more thoughtful, can contribute more and be more productive than our institutions allow them to demonstrate. Among my artichokes and cabbages, I determined that we as a business could and must do better.

Those ruminations eventually led to us becoming employee-owned in June 2018 and, perhaps more significantly, to committing to a program of introspection, coaching and learning that is progressively giving us the confidence to trust each other more, share information more freely and make decisions as locally and quickly as possible. That is the 'hope' of the title. I hope that the 'vegetables' and 'soil' are more self-explanatory.

We have organised the book roughly according to the seasons as we experience them as veg-growers and cooks): Veg New Year (May-July), Summer Flush (July-September), Autumn Plenty (September-November), Winter Chill (November-March), Hungry Gap (March-May). I hope the reassurance I find in the familiar seasonal recurrence of themes doesn't become repetitive. Newsletters with no seasonal reference are scattered at random and we round off with a few rants on topics close to my heart (mostly repeated from our first Riverford Farm Cookbook).

I am dyslexic and, in consequence, a slow reader, so taking 300 pages to say what could be said in thirty drives me nuts, especially when applied to business. So this is intentionally a short book of very short pieces. Even at this length I would be amazed if many people read it cover to cover. I hope it sits by the loo or the bath and you dip in and out and deem it worth the (recycled) paper. If any of its contents lead you to reconsider the nature of good farming or business I will be happy.

My thanks go to: my patient and supportive sister Rachel, whose editing has saved me from myself on many occasions; my managers who put up with my resistance to structure, my questioning of their value and my lifelong opposition to the word "professional"; to Rob, our MD for his constancy and balance in the face of my petulance and, most of all, to all the longstanding customers whose support has allowed us to be brave, sometimes foolhardy and to farm and run a business our way.

Guy Singh-Watson, Riverford Founder

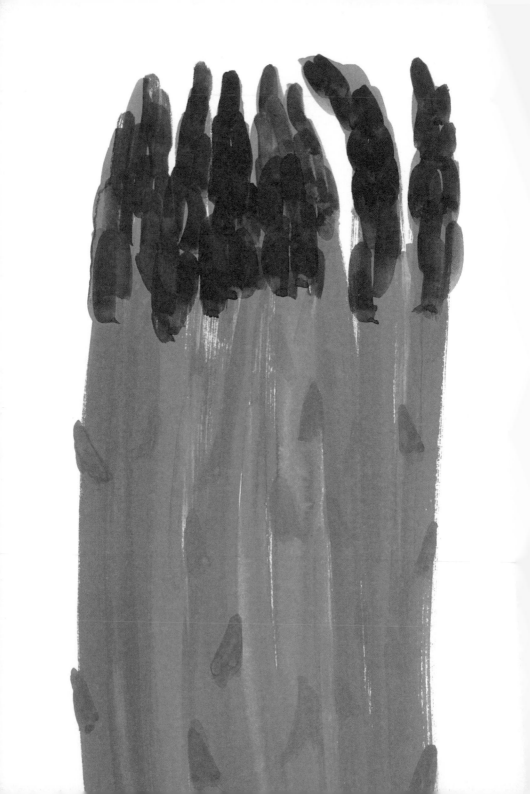

the veg new year

Hurrah, out with the old, the woody and the tired;
in with the first shoots of asparagus, cardoons,
rhubarb and wild garlic. The hungry gap edges to
a close. The first harvests of early potatoes, salads,
peas, broad beans, radishes, kohl rabi, cucumbers,
greens aplenty and strawberries proclaim the
arrival of another vegetable new year.

silage & sandcastles

The mower is humming along in the field outside, cutting silage*
for my brother's cows, hoping to make use of a brief break in the
weather. Thankfully we don't make nearly as much fuss about
it as they do on the Archers*. It is incredible how the machinery
has improved in the last twenty-five years. It used to take a month
of dawn-to-dusk days to take the first cut, by which time it was
almost time to start again on the second cut. Now it can all be
done in three days.

On the down side, there are no teas brought out by the
farmer's wife and shared in the field. The farmer's wife is more
often than not off earning more than the farmer. Contractors
work absurd hours on enormous machines to try and make ends
meet in an industry which is having the life squeezed out of it.
Instead of a shared tea propped up against the silent tractor, it's
a garage sandwich in the cab and a chat over the Citizens Band
radio. There may be a few pints in the Sea Trout after the clamp*
is sealed on the final day but there is no doubt that some of the
soul has left farming and many of the farmers are leaving with it.

At Riverford we try to put some of the soul back. Our co-op
has helped twelve family farms to survive, and, added to our own
farm, has generated over a hundred jobs. I had hoped to build
a restaurant on the farm where our staff plus customers, schools
and the public could share and enjoy the food produced in the
surrounding fields. It was to be my sandcastle in the rising tide
of anonymous, sanitised, over-processed, over-packaged, poor-
quality food sold to an increasingly obese population with no

idea that strawberries are in season in June. Sadly some neighbours, worried that such a project might disturb their rural idyll, have objected vociferously and planning permission has been refused. The sandcastle has slumped a bit but I plan to appeal. It really should be on the Archers and would certainly be more relevant to the struggles of a changing agriculture than which field David Archer should cut first.

enlightenment among the cabbages

One of the things I love about being an organic grower is the constant challenge. The ever-receding horizon of perfect knowledge means that I will be learning to the end. After thirty years, my assumptions are still regularly confounded in the field; in this case, why the cabbages won't grow. Pre-Enlightenment, our inability to explain natural phenomenon led to mysticism. I don't rule out that the crop is stunted due to the phase of the moon when it was planted, or that I failed to bury a corn dolly last autumn or to regularly prostrate myself before the appropriate deity, or didn't apply activated carbon or mineral dust.

Whatever the reason, our pointed cabbages do seem to have lost their spirit; like a whippet with its tail between its legs they seem nervous, unable to break out of themselves and get on with photosynthesising, growing and being eaten by you. As I stand among them, I am still searching for a more prosaic, scientifically conventional explanation. They have had the muck, the sun, the warmth and the water. The soil is not compacted and the weeds and pests are under control, so their purple leaves and pinched appearance remain a mystery.

After work and a few beers, I am still deliberating with the farm team. The consensus is that it's down to a mixture of things, all of a post-Enlightenment nature. Marco leads on stress brought on by wildly fluctuating temperatures; Scott on leaching of nutrients by February's rains, plus too long spent in the seed trays waiting for a break in the weather to allow planting; Didier thinks they have been too dry. We've sent some leaves off for analysis but don't expect anything conclusive – just another piece in the ever-evolving jigsaw. My enduring faith is that every year we will understand more, and become better farmers and custodians of the land as a result. Conventional* farmers might reach for a dose of ammonium nitrate to attempt to alleviate the immediate symptoms, but this contributes little to understanding the complex relationship of plant, soil, weather and just possibly the cosmos. There is no harm in accepting imperfect knowledge and occasional inexplicable failure; the enforced humility does us good. Though that sounds like something from *The Pilgrim's Progress*, it actually reflects a healthy post-Enlightenment acceptance that there is more to learn.

why I do it organically

I admit it; I farm organically largely because it just feels right. Is that an admission of weakness? I have a science degree, my tractors use GPS, and I wholeheartedly embrace the IT revolution. But I still find that what feels right is a good aid to making good decisions. Some condemn being guided by emotion as weak-minded, muddled thinking – which it sometimes is. But over the thirty years since I started farming organically, much of what *felt* wrong in farming has turned out to *be* wrong for very tangible, logical and scientific reasons.

Decisions that don't use what feels right as a sanity check can be just as dangerous as emotional decisions made without checking the measurable evidence. I do have concerns about selecting evidence to support a predetermined emotional bias, but what brings me back to the debate and makes me such a big mouth is frustration with the far more pervasive tendency to select evidence to support a commercial bias; something our agrochemical industry are masters of. Take the example of the 'world's favourite herbicide', glyphosate. In my early days as an organic grower I really missed glyphosate, which kills every part of the weed without the need for costly, soil-damaging ploughing. Given a free rein, my own standards would have included the occasional use of glyphosate, had I not been restrained by organic rules. But I would have been wrong. I am retrospectively grateful for what seemed like an illogical restraint at the time. There is now strong evidence that glyphosate is safe neither for users nor for the environment, and debate rages in Europe over whether it should be banned.

History has told this story again and again – so-called 'safe' pesticides are later banned. To be organic sometimes feels extreme, even provocative to chemical-using neighbouring farmers. Yet I am confident that time will reveal the 'extremists' are not the organic farmers, but those who use mind-bogglingly toxic chemicals with such casual abandon; that science will justify those who embraced ecology, rather than those who exploited incomplete knowledge of how to disrupt life without the humility to appreciate the risks.

slugs, ducks & a perfect spring

Well, with the downpour this week, at least my father hasn't been talking any more about the drought of '76. I should never have listened to him anyway. Next he will be talking about the storms of '47. I think we have had almost three inches of rain so far, which has been very welcome.

Our crops, almost without exception, are looking fantastic – probably the best I have ever seen them at this time of year. A few of the fleeces* have blown off and it has been too wet and windy to gather them in or put them back on. Now that the winds are in the south and there is plenty of moisture some of them could come off anyway.

The strawberries are flowering and looking good. We should be picking the very first berries by the end of the month. I am a bit concerned about the proliferation of slugs and have decided to commandeer a flock of ducks. We did this in the polytunnels one year, to great effect, until they all waddled off down to the river never to return. It is hard to believe, but they seem to love to get a crop full of the slimy pests.

How to find a flock of ducks! I tried the paper. I tried the free ads. I even tried the internet. It is rather reassuring to have discovered that, in the end, the best place to buy a duck is in the pub. I should say to be promised a duck because, like so much pub talk, it may come to nothing. Of course, I now also have the benefit of no end of advice as to the best breeds, ages, management etc. There are those who reckon I would be better with quails or guinea fowl so I might just try them too.

an aphid's view

If things are this good why grow wings, why even move? Why have sex and risk producing variable babies that may not be as good as me? Sexual reproduction is so full of uncertainty. Why not just stay put, plug in, suck that sweet, sweet sap and pour out a stream of babies identical to me through parthenogenesis*?

They need only shake free of my abdomen, plug in and enjoy the same good life. Within five days the young'uns will be squeezing out their own; it's perfect.

Two weeks ago, looking around the peppers on our farm in France I calculated that about twenty million wingless aphids were sucking the life out of my crop.

Each leaf had up to ten mothers with a stream of look-a-likes plugging in within millimetres of them. Marco, my ever-calm agronomist, told me not to worry: "I'm on top of it," he said. The temptation for the macho and inexperienced would be to wade in with some soap spray (restricted but permissible under organic regulations), which effectively suffocates the aphids it touches. But this would also risk killing the predators already feasting on the aphids and destroy our chances of reaching the holy grail of organic pest control – balance. Marco's policy was to wash off the worst colonies with water and introduce more ladybirds to mop up the rest. I was nervous; a ladybird can eat 5000 aphids in its life but can't compete with their reproduction rate. Who would eat their way to the top? As well as ladybirds we often seek help from my favourite aphid predator, *Aphidius colemani*. This tiny parasitic wasp deposits a single egg in each aphid. The baby wasp slowly digests the aphid from within, before emerging two weeks later, alien-style, as an adult ready to lay another 200 eggs. We introduced some of them for good measure.

Two weeks later, Marco was proved right. The ladybirds won and it looks like we will have a good, if slightly delayed, crop of peppers. Having seen the scenario played out so many times since we gave up spraying soap on aphids fifteen years ago, I should have had more faith in the under-promoted virtue of using less and understanding more. If a fraction of the money spent on pesticides and GM* crops went into studying agroecology, most insecticide use could be avoided.

ROUND ONE

piecework &
heisenburg's principles

Half the staff are lost in the broad beans, picking with deft, nimble and (I hope) well-motivated fingers, moving systematically up the rows like marshalled locusts. A bean top rustles now and then and occasionally a head pops up to carry out a completed crate, but otherwise they could all be asleep in there. Most veg is picked and packed on a piecework basis; so much per crate, row or kilo, and there is no doubt that this is the cheapest way to get a simple and uniform (and hence easily quantifiable) job done by poorly-motivated staff. One could say that this is fairer on the quicker pickers and some of our staff argue for it at meetings.

I have resisted because, when we tried it, my abiding memory of piecework was of the misery it causes. There was once even a punch-up between two crusty travellers over who had filled a bag of carrots. When they left I tipped it out to find that it was half-full of earth anyway; everyone intent on ripping off everyone else. Disputes were frequent, comradeship lost and less-experienced workers got so obsessed by how much they were making that they often wore themselves out before lunch. You can't put a price on something without changing its meaning. Art, scenery, lunch, life, vegetables and work; just about everything apart from money itself has an element that defies monetary valuation. Heisenburg's uncertainty principle (more frequently applied to wave motion) states that you cannot know two properties to arbitrary precision – measurement of one changes the other. Finite measurement of the monetary value of work denigrates the experience of it; one could say the same of many things.

I'm not sure what they would make of Heisenburg's principle in the bean patch. They all think I'm crazy anyway and it could be a challenge to explain it in English, Polish and Russian. No-one who actually does repetitive physical work for long subscribes to the patronising 'nobility of work' crap espoused by some not obliged to do it, but if you find yourself out there bent double it is better not to be continually reminded of the exact number of pounds and pence you are making compared to your neighbour. It takes a lot of effort to regulate and administrate piecework because the inbuilt assumption is that if you can rip someone off, you will. Instead we put that effort into treating staff with respect and making the work as rewarding as possible. Mostly it works; I haven't found anyone asleep in the hedge for a while.

fifty years at riverford

*As Jubilee celebrations build, John Watson reflects
on his fifty years' farming at Riverford.*

I had been farming Riverford's 120 acres for only a few months at
the time of the Queen's Coronation in 1953. Food was still rationed
and I brought the first tractor onto the farm. I got the tenancy on
the strength of a post-war degree in agriculture that championed
newness, efficiency and science. This made me a keen advocate
of all the technological wonders of the agricultural revolution.

Disillusionment gradually set in with the effect these practices
had on the crops on our thin Devon slopes and on animal welfare
and health. Even though our acreage grew to 500, there seemed no
opportunity for more than one successor to follow me into farming.

My son Ben was the first to return, he opened a farm shop,
inheriting his mother's joy in preparing food. Guy, disillusioned
with city 'yuppiedom', soon joined him to start his own business
growing vegetables.

Louise's equestrian career was terminated by a broken back
and she joined the farm partnership. Oliver then joined too, and
amalgamated the two dairy herds into one of 250 cows. Only
Rachel has made her life away from the farm.

All the land has been farmed organically since 1986. I have
been gratified to see the improvement in fertility and productivity,
proving the principles of organic farming. All the businesses have
grown, with another farm shop at Yealmpton, and Riverford
Organic Farmers marketing the produce of 600 acres of our
own land and that of twelve other farms in South Devon

Organic Producers Cooperative*. Most recently, Oliver has started a business processing and marketing our organic milk.

How wrong I was to think there was room for only one successor! The family now offers employment to up to 150 – and customer spending circulates in the local economy, bringing further benefits to the revival of our part of the countryside.

Riverford now employs about 650 people.

a happy farmer

I am generally a glass-half-empty man and as a result, a bit of a miserable bugger. It's the cost of my constant quest to find something that is wrong and think how it could be done better. This morning, having done a few hours in the fields, I have rejected the hot office in favour of a seat on the pontoon, balancing a laptop, with my feet dangling in the irrigation reservoir.

I could worry about the fact that my toes only just touch the water; last week it was up to my calves. Should this wonderful weather continue we will be diving into mud by August. Until then we are able to irrigate, but for many of our growers the veg fits in around cows and sheep and they have not invested the thousand pounds an acre it costs in ponds, pipes and pumps. I could worry about the potential feud between our Polish workers (suspected of eating the carp in the lake) and the English coarse-fishing enthusiasts who like to catch them after work, stroke them and put them back. I could even worry about dropping my laptop in the water.

But as I look out over the reservoir, watching the swallows dip for a casual drink (or is it to feed on larvae?) and witnessing the dragonflies copulating in flight, with the dog rose (my favourite flower) rambling over the hedges in full bloom, it is hard not to see that glass as almost full. We have had a great start to the year and I am almost as content as the wood pigeon cooing behind me. There you go, it's a myth – farmers don't always moan, and that was the quickest newsletter I have ever written.

northerly winds, love & wendell berry

The new growing year has started with a blissfully dry and bright spring and no major gales, frosts or pestilence. Most crops were planted into perfect seedbeds and are doing well; a few are even ahead of schedule, helped by super-light fleece* covers which retain moisture and keep off the recently prevalent northerly winds. The swallows have only just arrived, a month later than last year, presumably delayed by those dry winds.

With so little to moan about, let me instead recommend those with time to listen to an exceptionally good Start the Week on BBC Radio 4, entitled *Wendell Berry: The Natural World*, in which Andrew Marr interviews this delightfully drawling 82-year-old poet and Kentucky farmer. The discussion is marked by a refreshing humility and refusal to bow down to the "grown up" notion, prevalent in economics, politics and neo-environmentalism, that the world can only be measured in, and guided by, hard numbers. Above all there was an acknowledgement of love; if we can't admit to loving our surroundings, whether people, nature or food, how can we care for them? Love, often written off as a childish, romantic or unaffordable emotion, provides a more powerful motive to care for what we value than the fiscal incentives favoured by economists and politicians. Despite Berry reading perhaps one of the most depressing poems ever written (which he quickly and endearingly acknowledges), I urge you to listen. As a society we no doubt need a few numbers to check our more outlandish emotions, but I long for a world shaped by love over one which denigrates the unmeasurable, and will fight for it unashamedly in the boardroom, in my fields and in this newsletter.

competition, collaboration & car manufacture

Last week we were visited by some of our growers from Andalusia. For years they've produced veg for us that we can't grow at home without heating with fossil fuels. As I approached Pepe, who this year has grown the spinach and asparagus which precedes the UK crop, I extended my hand with typical English reserve, only to be pulled into an extended Andalusian embrace. After six years, what started as a trading relationship has developed into a lasting friendship; one that's benefitted us and our box customers and will, I expect, see one or both of us into retirement.

The contrast couldn't be greater with our (now long past) annual trips as suppliers to supermarket HQ: having scrubbed up for the nightmare session of abuse from a buyer, the visit would start with the ritualistic humiliation of a two-hour wait (calculated to soften you up) before finally we would be summoned to meet the latest testosterone-charged buyer. Thankfully, that was fifteen years ago, but I gather things at some supermarkets haven't changed much.

Does business have to be done like this? After thirty years of trying to find an efficient and courteous alternative, I have reluctantly come to the conclusion that competition is pretty good at driving innovation and improvement. Brutal as it sounds, if you don't have the incentive to find a way of both doing what you have to do today, and doing it a little bit better tomorrow, it's only a matter of time before someone else does and your number is up.

This is not to accept that short-term, cut-throat dealmaking is the best way. A school friend has spent his working life making parts for the automotive industry. I'm always amazed to hear how the larger car manufacturers, having selected a partner, invest heavily in making the relationship work, in the long run and for both parties. Car manufacture must be one of the most competitive and sophisticated industries in the world; it is heartening that there, like Pepe and me, they have reached the conclusion that building and maintaining relationships is critical to long-term success.

samphire, ospreys & trench foot

For many years we have picked marsh samphire from a salt marsh formerly used as summer grazing by the Miller family, one of our farming co-op members. For two centuries a sea wall originally built by Napoleonic prisoners of war held back the tidal waters of the River Erme – before being breached ten years ago. Natural England* decided to preserve the flooded fields as a salt marsh and when the saltwater killed the grass and trees, the ground was quickly colonised by tiny seeds of marsh samphire carried in the water.

The Millers lost seventy acres of highly-prized summer grazing, but gained a modest source of income over the past few years as their sons and friends foraged the deliciously succulent salty spears of samphire each summer, which we sell alongside your veg boxes. Joe Miller has now had enough of dodging the tides and kneeling in the mud for hours. Picking is incredibly fiddly, whether armed with a small knife, a pair of scissors or Joe's favoured garden shears. This year, pending reapproval from Natural England, my son and his mates (who foraged wild garlic for us in the Easter holidays) have taken on some of the picking as they finish their A-levels. The marsh is remote and beautiful with just ducks and the occasional osprey for company. A nimble-fingered picker in a good patch might manage to harvest two kilos an hour before being driven off the marsh by the incoming tide; this then has to be hauled a quarter of a mile to the nearest vehicle access. As the ecology of the marsh has evolved, a succession of more competitive perennial species has colonised it and the less vigorous annual samphire has declined, so this may well be the last year of harvesting here.

We are trying to arrange picking from a much larger marsh in Essex, in which case there may be enough to include in the veg boxes themselves; otherwise (assuming the boys don't get trench foot and wimp out) there will be modest quantities to add to your order over the next three weeks. Samphire is traditionally eaten with fish or occasionally lamb, but I like it best blanched for four minutes and served alongside an omelette or scrambled eggs. Either way, in my book the trickiness of harvesting this crop makes it all the more of a culinary prize.

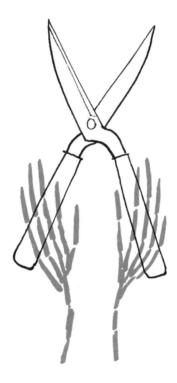

in search of an environmentally-acceptable tomato

The strawberries are ripening well and this week will see the addition of celery, new potatoes and cucumbers to the lengthening list of our own produce in the boxes, but even with the recent sunshine our first unheated tomatoes are still green and two weeks from harvest. The only way to get local tomatoes earlier is by using heat. Our research has led us to the conclusion that heated glass is almost as crazy as airfreight and, although we have some very good growers that we like working with, sanity calls for a change. The ideal would be to convince you to forgo tomatoes, peppers, cucumbers and aubergines for eight months of the year from November to June, but my ad hoc survey of the fridges of even the most eco-conscious of my friends invariably reveals a winter weakness.

Trucking a kilo of peppers from Spain causes about 300 grams of CO_2 emissions. Growing them out of season in heated glass in Northern Europe results in about fifteen times as much, at 4.5 kilos of CO_2 per kilo of fruit. The sum is only marginally better for tomatoes – which is why I am typing this in the back of a Spaniard's car, swerving through the olive groves and sunflower fields of Andalusia. To coin an M&S-ism, we don't want just any tomato. We need to know that it will taste good and be grown and transported in a way that is genuinely considerate of environmental and social issues.

Most Spanish winter production is from the hideous sea of plastic blighting the coast between Almeria and Malaga.

But a little further east, in the relatively unscathed Cabo de Gata National Park, there is a group of organic growers led by Paco Ramon. With his three brothers, and three generations of inherited experience, he coaxes life from the sand using sheep muck invigorated with essence of grape skins. It is the tail end of their season but the tomatoes tasted pretty good so, all being well, it will be largely Paco's tomatoes in the boxes this winter.

deluge, drought & distilling doctors

Yes, the whingeing farmers are whingeing again. We have had two inches of rain in two months now. For most of those two months there have been strong, dry, northerly winds which sucked those two inches out of the soil again in next to no time. The sunshine has been glorious, but we do desperately need a couple of days of our notoriously dismal, damp, Devon drizzle.

As we get into summer, every week brings us a wider selection of vegetables from which to make up the boxes and they always taste so much better than the imports. Broad beans, sugar snap peas, courgettes, bunched carrots and squash, even the new-season cabbages, turnips and calabrese* have an invigorating freshness and are a joy to handle, cook and eat.

We once had an eccentric doctor who each spring would buy tonnes of immature broad beans from which he extracted a potion guaranteed to make you live to 150. We have not seen him for a few years so perhaps he was struck off. Nutty as he undoubtedly was, my primeval instincts tell me that if I eat enough of all these new-season vegetables, I may still be surfing at seventy.

MOWN

MOWN

MOWN

field banter &
music festivals

This is being written in the Vendée, where the courgettes are growing so quickly that we have to pick them every day and even then the field is littered with discarded marrows that got away from us. The specification (35-50mm diameter) is the source of much mirth; my French is not up to much and I struggle to follow the field banter, but it seems to centre around the women having a more realistic estimate of size. When the courgettes are finished it is onto the bunched carrots; here the jokes are all about "carottes amoureuses" where two roots have followed the same fissure down through the soil and become entwined. They are the happiest workforce I have ever known. The only other work around here is pulling the guts out of ducks at the local abattoir so perhaps it is not surprising that they seem so happy to be out in the fields.

I travelled here via London and the V&A where, amongst statues, jewels and porcelain, we collected the Observer Best Ethical Online Retailer award to add to the Best Ethical Business and Best Ethical Restaurant we won last year; most gratifying. Thanks to those of you who voted for us.

The yurt-housed Travelling Field Kitchen has been on the road for a month now, first in Hampshire and more recently at Freightliners City Farm in London. The food has been fantastic and the atmosphere harmonious and joyful. Logistically it is as difficult as getting a crusade to Jerusalem, but the contented hubbub of conversation from 80 well-fed diners reminds me why we embarked on this crazy project in the first place. At the end of July we take our yurt to WOMAD*. As well as running a pared-down version of the restaurant in the mornings, we are sponsoring the Taste the World stage where, after performing on the main stages, musicians from all over the world come to cook, tell stories and play the occasional song to small and intimate audiences before sharing food with them. If, like me, you are a bit crowd phobic, with an eclectic taste in music, I cannot recommend WOMAD highly enough; it is a very civilised experience.

monsanto, polar bears
& donald rumsfeld

The great virtue of glyphosate, the world's 'favourite' herbicide, is that it kills slowly and thoroughly; it disrupts amino acid synthesis in every cell, leading to plant death two weeks later. After converting to organic farming in the 1980s I missed it, but over the years we have found alternatives in stale seed beds*, cultivation techniques, and thermal and inter-row weeding*. Today, we generally control weeds effectively yet add only around 5 per cent to our production costs.

Forty-eight MEPs recently tested positive for glyphosate, with concentrations in their urine at between five and forty times the level considered acceptable in drinking water. The World Health Organisation has classified the chemical as a 'probable carcinogen' so, with the licence to sell and use glyphosate in Europe expiring this month, an argument is raging in Brussels over whether it should be renewed, and if so, under what terms. The evidence on either side is far from convincing but, predictably, the UK is for renewal. One would hope that a decision will be made based on an assessment of risks, rationally balanced against an assessment of benefits; but history (asbestos, DDT, dioxins, tobacco) suggests that we frequently underestimate risks stemming from what we just don't know. The majority of pesticides I used on the farm as a teenager, judged safe at the time by our regulators (largely based on science selected and paid for by the manufacturers), have subsequently been banned on health or environmental grounds, often after long wrangles like the one going on in Brussels right now.

Polychlorinated bipenyl (PCBs), another Monsanto* product, were judged too toxic for use by the US Navy in the 1950s but it took another twenty years for them to be banned. Today every one of us carries these hormone-disrupting carcinogens in our bodies. One study suggests they reduce polar bear reproduction by weakening their penises; no-one predicted that consequence and I don't suppose Monsanto will offer compensation. My point? When approving novel chemicals we need to consider what we don't know we don't know (what Donald Rumsfeld, ex-US secretary of defense, calls the 'unknown unknowns'), what we know we don't know ('known unknowns'), as well as what we know. This requires both caution and humility, rare qualities in those with political and economic power.

The result was a fudge. A five-year licence, rather than the usual fifteen, was granted in 2017, so the whole argument will start again soon.

exodus: not a good time for slugs

For the last month, our irrigation reservoirs have been rimmed by a black mass of writhing tadpoles. I reckon there are over a million in the one I swim in, even after the carp have feasted. Last week they got their legs and this week they are off; the ground around the ponds is heaving as they go in search of their first terrestrial meal. Facing this hungry biblical plague, slugs have no chance. It will be two years before the toads return to breed, by which time they'll have made a home on the waterless hill half a mile away.

"What we do about slugs?" is always the visiting gardener's top question on our organic farms. The answer, with the occasional exception in our polytunnels, is nothing; they aren't a problem for our field crops. I know you will find the occasional slimy surprise in our lettuces and our sprouts are often scarred (which we hope and assume you can live with), but I cannot remember ever seeing any organic crops suffering significantly. Most conventional* potato growers will routinely apply vast quantities of slug pellets and still have substantial damage. Likewise, slugs can be a huge problem in winter wheat and barley even after applying pellets, but almost never when the ground has been organic for three years or more. The reason is undoubtedly that our soils, free from pesticides and synthetic fertilisers, are teeming with life looking for a meal; toads, frogs and carabid beetles like to munch on slugs, nematodes* will parasitise them, and there are almost certainly many other predators and pathogens*. No-one makes money from their activity, so this unglamorous part of ecology hasn't been studied much.

The principle of organic farming is to find balance; the population of every indigenous pest (except *Homo sapiens*) is regulated by predators and pathogens. It doesn't always work; sometimes you have to encourage them a little (for example, flowering plants to foster the lacewings and hoverflies that control aphids), but with slugs all you have to do is spare the soil those toxic chemicals, and soil ecology will do the rest. Annoyingly I know this approach does not work in a garden; I suspect there is just too much cover for the slugs to retreat to. If you can handle the poo and keep the foxes away, get a duck.

JULY TO SEPTEMBER
summer flush

Heralded by the first courgette, with each week
bringing more veg into season; broad beans make
way for French and then runners. Our polytunnels
are dripping with tomatoes, peppers, chillies and
aubergines. Outside, beets, broccoli, carrots, fennel
artichokes and the first corn thrive, with long
days and plenty of sun packing flavour into our
vegetables. Salads, grills and barbecues beckon.

plants: not so dumb & passive

Much of horticulture is about managing the urge of plants to reproduce. Humans need and crave the more digestible, nutrient-dense food found in the reproductive parts of crops; that is the flowers, fruits, seeds, bulbs and tubers. As growers we devote ourselves to manipulating plants to maximise the yield and quality of those tender and tasty reproductive organs, which is a tricky balance to strike. If only we could sell you grass for your supper – alas the easy to grow, non-reproductive parts of plants are largely indigestible to humans.

Plants in their wild state have survived the challenges of pestilence, drought, flood and ice ages by mastering a long-term strategy of balancing growth and dominance against risk. Getting bigger to increase their reproductive capacity must be balanced against the risk of not making it to maturity. At a cellular level the strategy all boils down to whether a cell in the apical meristem (growing point) differentiates into leaf or flower (above ground) or into a root or starch-saving tuber (below). If things are looking good a plant will typically extend its vegetative life, assuming the chance for greater fecundity will come later; if things are getting tough (drought, lack of nutrients or light etc.) it will switch to sexual mode early so at least some genes are preserved.

Such were my musings as I observed our early runner beans which have grown and grown but failed to produce a crop. The generally-held wisdom is to build a strong plant, then stress it with water deprivation to make it flower, then give it everything it needs so it feels confident and fills every pod. As our plants reach for the polytunnel roof and the soil is covered with aborted flowers and just a few crates of beans to show for it, it's plain we haven't grasped the subtleties.

There is a tendency to regard plants as dumb and passive, yet their interaction with the world goes far beyond the basic tropisms* we learnt at school. They can sense, even 'hear' pest attack and respond with defence chemicals, much as our own immune system works. They may not moo, baa or rush around, but the apparent passivity of plants hides subtleties and complex responses which have served them well. It remains to be seen how well they will survive *Homo sapiens*.

potatoes & potato bores

At my nephew's twenty-first birthday last month, my niece had prepared a wonderful potato, broad bean and mint salad. When I smugly commented on how good the potatoes were, there was an embarrassed silence followed by the admission that she had bought them elsewhere because she didn't think our first earlies were very good. I was mortified and spent the afternoon in a sulk, and the next day trying to track down the origin and variety of the offending spuds.

We know from our limited market research that most of you rate flavour as the main reason for buying our veg boxes (ahead of the environment, lack of pesticides, convenience and support for local growers by a factor of two), so I feel justified in my nerdish pursuit of the perfect potato. The trouble with flavour is that it's subjective, hard to quantify and influenced by many factors such as variety, growing conditions, maturity at harvest and storage. Pushing crops on with too much water and nitrogen, as so frequently happens in conventional* farming, definitely leads to disappointment in the kitchen.

As with all management, measurement is the first step to improvement. Most fruit-and-veg-industry technical managers measure what can be quantified objectively (sugar content, degrees of bend in a banana etc.) and ignore the rest. John, my fellow in-house veg nerd, has gone further; he has assessed the taste buds of most of our staff to come up with a 'sensory evaluation panel'. I didn't qualify. Every couple of weeks this elite group sit down and mull over our more contentious fruit and veg in search of consensus. We want to know what produce the group likes and why, in the hope that we can correlate this with the variety, soil, growing method, etc. Last week it was strawberries and the tasters showed extraordinary accuracy in assessing firmness, acidity and sweetness – but, interestingly, the most significant preference criteria were the absence of 'soapiness' or cardamom flavours – not something that can be quantified objectively by industry scientists.

We are still arguing about potatoes. Our early varieties (mainly Ostara and Lady Crystal) are better than most, but have been variable and sometimes disappointing this year. The one consistency is the excellent but frustratingly slow-growing Charlotte (in the boxes from mid-July). Next year, spurred on by my niece, we'll try chitting* some of the Charlotte to bring them forward a fortnight.

tea, elixirs & faith

Despite studying natural sciences at university and absorbing all that Darwinian, evidence-based rationality, I like to think I am still an open-minded man. When Raphs, one of our longest-standing and more cosmically-attuned members of staff, suggested focussing positive energy on the artichokes using cups of aluminium filings and a copper wire I gave it a go (still awaiting results). I have sprayed my onions with liquid seaweed (seemed to work) and my cauliflowers with garlic extract (definitely didn't) without any concrete evidence of efficacy. One winter I even tried to wade my way through the endless, unfathomable sentences of Rudolf Steiner (the father of biodynamic* agriculture) in an attempt to get my head around why I should fill a cow horn with excrement and bury it for six months before diluting the contents and spraying it on my crops in the spring. I have not yet let the bloke from the pub, who claims to have invented perpetual motion, retune our tractor engines but I have bought him a drink; who knows, he might be a genius.

Over lunch today, John, our solid, sensible, Arsenal-supporting farm manager, told me he was spraying the drought-stricken celeriac with compost tea fermented from the worm casts*. Reading through the bumph, it seems it will improve yield, root development, disease resistance, colour and even eating quality; a true elixir in the best tradition of a catch-all cure. My dull, reductionist training immediately asks; how will it achieve these remarkable results? By inoculating the soil with beneficial microorganisms it would seem. It sounds like total tosh to me but we will give it a go. As an agnostic in need of evidence, I have suggested a control area be marked off for comparison.

Organic farmers are wholly dependent on the health of their soil. That soil is such a rich and complex ecosystem; a myriad of relationships between hundreds of thousands of different plants, bacteria, fungi and invertebrates as well as water, temperature and the soil minerals themselves. Science has barely begun to understand this complex underworld so it would be arrogant and foolhardy to write off anything that works just because we don't understand how or why. To deny the inexplicable would be to imply there is nothing new to learn. That would be dull.

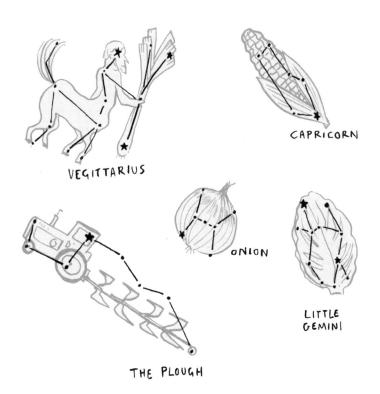

VEGITTARIUS

CAPRICORN

ONION

LITTLE GEMINI

THE PLOUGH

a uk-only box – but will anyone buy it?

In 1993, when we packed our first veg box, what little imported organic produce available was fit only for the compost heap by the time it got here, so our veg boxes were UK-only by default. Back then, organic box customers and organic growers alike were widely characterised as freaks on the fringe, prepared to pursue the principles of local and seasonal even if it meant a diet of cauliflower, stored roots and cabbage for months at a stretch.

Twenty-three years and thirty million veg boxes later, I am happy to be part of a broader church. While our veg is still around 80 per cent home-grown, it is supplemented by our French farm and a small grower group in Spain. Together they provide tomatoes, peppers and the like year-round without the environmental disaster that is UK, heated-glass production, and without losing the closeness to our growers. But globalisation has not passed organic farming by; if you want to buy organic and are not too worried about how or where it is produced, the supermarkets will provide you with just about anything at any time. Some of the organic pioneers whose advice I sought in the '80s would be delighted that trade and scale have led to success and accessibility, but I suspect more would be appalled by the way trade has so often prevailed over principles.

I reckon we strike a pretty good balance between principles and pragmatism in what we provide. Eating can be a political and philosophical act but mostly it is just eating, and I don't think it is our job to tell you what to eat (though we may nudge you in the direction of a sustainable as well as pleasurable diet and do draw the line at things like airfreight). Having said that, many of you have a strong preference for home-grown veg and I do get a regular ear-bashing from the hardliners for importing at all, so we are going to offer a 100 per cent-UK box again. Our last attempt amounted to just 1 per cent of sales, but maybe things have changed and more of us are willing to do without peppers for longer. We plan to run this box across the year – bar a break for the hungry gap, when only the hardest of the hard core would be satisfied with its limited contents.

The timing of this may strike some as politically ill-judged. I can only say that we value our close relations with our French and Spanish growers – and that this was planned way before the EU referendum!

in it for the long haul

The papers are full of stories of the newly-impoverished middle classes turning away from organic food in general and box schemes in particular. Add to that rising fuel prices, and the media would have you believe that we veg-box growers are ready to end it all in a puff of shotgun smoke. For several years the media have painted a story of unimpeded boom; now it is one of fathomless doom.

As always, the truth is a bit more complex. We, and most other box schemes, are having a pretty hard time. In fact, despite the widely-professed enthusiasm for all things local, seasonal and organic, this has been the case for a year or more. The new austerity has certainly played a part, but more significant are public confusion and exhaustion in the face of a barrage of well-funded but poorly-substantiated environmental and ethical claims made by every retailer, manufacturer and political party. We are being squeezed out of our well-earned place in the minds of less established and more uncertain customers by a tidal wave of bullshit. This is frustrating but, given the sheer volume of these claims, perhaps not surprising.

By my reckoning, if you are hard up, want to save the planet and love your food, staying in and cooking from a veg box is the smart thing to do. You could probably save a pound or two by buying the cheapest non-organic veg, but by the time you have fought your way through the traffic, checkout queues and packaging you will probably need a glass or two to restore your good humour – that's before cooking it and suffering the bland fare.

In the meantime, I want to reassure you that neither we nor any of our co-op members intend to give up, sell out, reach for the chemicals or blow our brains out. We had our staff summer party at Riverford last weekend; a twelve-hour, lakeside feast of wine, beer, food, volleyball, swimming, football and music. I wish all our customers could have been there to share in it. Over twenty-two years I have noticed that staff parties and ad hoc conversations with customers are better barometers of an organisation's prospects than accounts and sales figures. This was the best party we have had for years.

25TH JULY 2011

localism, pragmatism & the two pacos

Three years ago, based on an environmental study with Exeter University, we took the decision to phase out our use of tomatoes, peppers and cucumbers from heated glasshouses, however local. Maintaining a temperature of 20°C in single-glazed glasshouses in frosty January is completely insane; these were easily the most environmentally-damaging crops we sold. Without heat we can plant in polytunnels in April and start picking in July, giving us an unheated UK season of twelve weeks for tomatoes, fourteen for cucumbers and about ten for peppers, before the quality declines with falling temperatures and light in October.

So what do we do for the other forty weeks of the year when, understandably, most customers still want tomatoes? Much as we will always champion what's in season and put it in the boxes until you start begging for respite, Riverford would have gone under without some pragmatic supplementation. Contrary to the popular enthusiasm for localism, we have moved our out-of-season tomato production from West-Country hothouses to two Andalusian growers, both of them called Paco. Each can grow through the winter without heat, and the emissions from transporting their tomatoes to the UK (about 240g of CO_2 per kilo of fruit) are around a tenth of those associated with growing them closer to home using heat. We selected the Pacos on the basis of flavour (of their tomatoes) and personality (we like and trust them), and have worked with them to improve their tomatoes further through variety choice and growing techniques. We still have a way to go, but after three years I am now proud of our out-of-season tomatoes and peppers about 80 per cent of the time (up from a dismal 20 per cent when we started).

A bigger challenge has been to find local growers willing to grow for a shorter season without heat. Despite the savings in fuel, it is hard to build a business requiring such specialist skills and equipment around such a short harvesting window. In the end we decided to do it ourselves. After a year of haggling with planners, this week we start work on building three acres of sophisticated plastic-skinned green houses, which will grow tomatoes and cucumbers in the summer and salad leaves in the winter. When they are in production we will have the best-tasting, lowest-impact salads money can buy.

no pockets in a shroud

Twenty-five years ago, as I helped load seed potatoes with Gordon Strutt, an older, gentler and wiser neighbour, he advised me, "There are no pockets in a shroud, Guy". My business was starting to take off and I was probably a bit smug; at eighty, his was winding down but he showed no rancour at my success.

Ten years later, having inspired a generation of local growers, Gordon had joined his beloved potatoes underground and Riverford had grown manyfold, but his words stayed with me. The sale of another veg box scheme, Abel & Cole, to venture capitalists brought a stream of bankers to our door, all promising to lubricate my exit into well-heeled retirement. Building Riverford has been an intensely personal, creative endeavour; exhausting, but hugely rewarding. As I once explained to a banker before showing him the door, to sell Riverford as a tradable chattel, whose purpose would become to maximise short-term returns for external investors, would be tantamount to selling one of my children into prostitution.

I love my job and am a long way from hanging up the hoe, but through the recession, as the chaos resulting from greed grew, so did my interest in finding a better form of long-term ownership. Initially I was driven by a leftward-leaning idealism; more recently, with a growing distrust of all ideological dogma, my motivation has come from a frustration that most external, profit-hungry ownership results in short-term, narrow-minded management practices that are poor at harnessing our human potential.

Having visited many employee-owned companies I have found little narrow dogma. They have been as diverse in their ideologies as in their activities, but united in a desire to find a way to combine a better form of ownership with enlightened management which gets the most out of people. They also share a refreshingly optimistic view of humanity – that most of us, most of the time are as good as our organisations allow us to be. I want Riverford to be part of that better, kinder, optimistic world. Like Gordon, I'll be part of Riverford until I join my veg underground, but the plan is for employees who have helped create it to own most of it well before I go.

14TH AUGUST 2006
ranting from the fringe

I am not sure whether to respond with pride or irritation to Tesco and Sainsbury's synchronous announcement last week that both will be starting organic veg box schemes this autumn. It is becoming hard to be a maverick when, like an insatiable amoeba, mainstream capitalism constantly morphs to imitate and subsume any successful enterprise on the fringes.

The organic market accounts for less than 2 per cent of groceries and, as such, its direct influence on farming and retailing is obviously limited. It has had much more influence indirectly, by demonstrating that a more sensible method of agriculture is both possible and, for a growing number of households, desirable. Just as nine years of Labour rule forced the Conservatives to abandon some of their more belligerent policies, so the real-world success of organic farming – even on a relatively small scale – has forced the remaining 98 per cent of agriculture to move from outright ridicule to a level of acceptance. Box schemes and farmers' markets now seem to be similarly influencing mainstream supermarkets.

For twenty years, the obsession with cheapness and customer choice showed scant regard for flavour, seasonality, provenance, the environment or socio-economic impact on suppliers and communities. Ironically the pursuit of choice has produced uniformity, as the diversity represented by smaller, less commercially-focused producers is driven out. There is passion, creativity and innovation on the fringes; farmers' markets, box schemes and organic farming were born out of this. They were a direct response to the madness of our mainstream system of food production and retailing and have found growing resonance with customers who do not find fulfilment wandering aisles stocked with tens of thousands of over-packaged, over-travelled and seasonless products.

Now the lumbering amoeba is trying to expand and gobble up us and other box schemes, its appetite whetted by the corner of the grocery market it has not yet conquered, and by a slavish whoring after current enthusiasm for environmentalism and ethical business. Will it get us? We will see. I think it may find that running a box scheme requires a set of skills and above all a trust and understanding of growers and customers which are outside its vocabulary – however sophisticated its skills in logistics, supplier-management and market research. 'Responding to customers' has its place, but I am not sure it is enough. I get the sense that our customers want us to stand up for what we think is right, even if that is sometimes not popular and may not be immediately commercially viable.

bees & bad farming

In 2013, after years of campaigning from both sides of the divide, the EU finally voted to ban neonicotinoid insecticides on crops attractive to bees. Numerous studies suggest these are linked to collapsing bee numbers, and for once it seemed that environmental concerns had been put ahead of commercial interests (albeit reluctantly in the UK, where our government fought the ban to the end).

Last week, caving into pressure from the National Farmers' Union and pesticide manufacturers, the Department for Environment, Food & Rural Affairs temporarily overturned the ban in Suffolk, Cambridgeshire, Bedfordshire and Hertfordshire. The justification was the NFU's claim that growing oilseed rape was "becoming impossible" due to attacks by flea beetle*. It turns out that related losses amounted to just 3.5 per cent of the crop last year; not quite my definition of "impossible", but deemed by our government to be more important than bees. It would seem that the decision was not even supported by their own pesticide advisers who have been gagged, with minutes of meetings kept secret.

We lose crops to flea beetle at Riverford, but the severity of the attack declines later in the summer. By the time that oilseed rape is being sown – in August and September – I am surprised they are deemed such a problem. In our experience, rain falling as seedlings emerge is normally enough to suppress flea beetle activity and get a crop away, and it is soon strong enough to outgrow any damage. In the case of oilseed rape, the wide potential sowing window leaves plenty of time to re-sow in September if you are unlucky. Looking at rape crops from train windows, I would suggest that waterlogging and poor soil structure (normally the result of bad farming) are much more serious causes of crop loss.

I can't help noticing that the four counties judged to be worst-affected by flea beetle happen to be the ones with the fewest hedges and trees, the largest fields, the least grass and species diversity and the greatest prevalence of annual monocultures. Like all insects, flea beetles have natural predators in a diverse countryside but very few in the ecological desert of intensive arable farms. Could this be a problem farmers have brought on themselves by their own bad farming? Now bees and the rest of us are paying the price.

weeds, tomatillos &
too many farming adages

It is said that "the difference between a good and a bad farmer is a week"; timing is critical. While pulling three-foot-high fat hen, redshank and nightshade weeds from a crop of flageolet beans on our farm in France this morning, I had cause to reflect on this. Weeding a week earlier would have halved the work and doubled the effectiveness. Indeed, we wrote off the worst half of the field – the beans would never pay for the labour, especially as much of the damage to the crop had already been done. Good farmers murder their weeds, whether with hoes or chemicals, when young and vulnerable. These brutes took both hands to uproot and brought half the bean crop with them – back-wrenching, blistering work in the summer sun.

Weed-ridden crops yield less due to the competition, are slower to harvest and are often of poor quality. Worse still, the weeds shed seeds which plague us for years to come . . . "one year's seeding brings seven years' weeding" is another tediously true adage. With twenty-five years' experience we have become masters of weed control in Devon, but here in the Vendée we lost concentration while busy picking, and are paying the price.

Of course, "a weed is just a plant in the wrong place" (yet another adage). Ironically most of our crops have their origins in plants which could be described as weeds – before breeders selected for yield, uniformity etc., and in the process lost much of the vigour which made them successful as weeds. But it's little consolation for our half-abandoned bean field.

Tomatillos are to Mexicans what tomatoes are to Italians. After trials in Devon last year, we decided to grow them here in France; they were too wild and unruly for our orderly Devon polytunnels. Tomatillos are the size of a small tomato, have a firm texture and tangy, citrus sweetness. They can be eaten raw but are normally cooked in Mexico where they are in everything: soups, stews, barbeques, but most of all in the ubiquitous salsa verde, where they combine with chilli, garlic and coriander to excellent effect. They will be on the extras list from next week. I urge you to try them.

cooking with love

Cooking from scratch takes time. Sometimes it seems futile cooking for hours and then dragging the family to the table for a stressful meal before arguing about whose turn it is to do the washing up. Why not reach for the oven chips and frozen pizza, or just let them graze from the fridge at will?

Occasionally, appreciation or good-humoured conversation proves it's all worthwhile. While quizzing our fifteen-year-old daughter on the food she had eaten on her exchange trip to France, she inadvertently paid the greatest compliment that any kitchen-bound parent could hope for; though she liked the food and commented favourably on the way it was shared around a table, something was missing compared with our chaotic meals at home. After a few moments musing she said, with the poignancy and directness that only children have, "it was not made with love". Parenting can be hard at times, but that made up for a month of tantrums and sibling disagreements. Intuitively we all know that sharing a meal made with love nourishes more than the body, but it is great to be told.

Food is an intrinsic part of any healthy culture and is worth investing in. Last weekend we sponsored the 'Taste the World' stage at WOMAD*. After performing on the main stages, artists from all corners of the globe cooked their favourite dishes in our tent while playing the occasional song and discussing the relationship of food, family and music – and then sharing their meal with the audience.

I am not good in crowds, so it was with some trepidation that I took the family to my first festival in twenty years. Part of the deal was that we provide the veg and do our own cookery demonstrations (fortunately without the songs). This was made even more scary after witnessing the charm and style of a guitar-playing Louisiana beauty cooking gumbo. For the most part I reckon I was a better cook (some of the North African performers conceded that it was the women in their lives who did the cooking), but it is hard to compete with someone who can not only cook for a crowd, but sing, speak eight languages and play a range of instruments, most of which I had never seen before. It was a fantastic weekend and reaffirmed my conviction that real food, prepared with love from wholesome ingredients, has an international cultural significance to be embraced.

the limits of science

Contrary to most of the press coverage, the Food Standards Agency's report, published last week, did not prove that organic food was no better for you than non-organic. It merely showed that there was no conclusive evidence either way, on the grounds of a limited review of existing research into a limited range of nutrients taken in isolation. It did not touch on the effects of the pesticide contamination routinely found in almost half of conventional* fruit and veg. Nor did it touch on the effect of the massive use of antibiotics that props up an intensive pig and poultry industry. It did not even touch on the well-proven benefits to biodiversity and the lower carbon footprint of organic food, or the higher standards of animal welfare.

Even the very limited area of its study is at odds with the preliminary findings of a much larger £125 million pan-European study involving thirty universities and research institutes. I find myself questioning why £120,000 of our money has been spent regurgitating old research by a government quango that is supposed to ensure food safety, undermining a form of farming that is patently safer for farmers, safer for the environment and safer for consumers. What is it about organic farming that the food industry finds so threatening? We and our customers are a pretty harmless bunch. The worst that could happen is that history proves us misguided – though history seems to repeatedly show that it is the hasty and blinkered commercial application of narrow science to food and farming that is proving misguided. Since leaving agricultural college 25 years ago I have seen most of the pesticides, and many of the additives previously declared safe by the government, banned due to their threat to health or the environment.

It is incredibly difficult to design a study of sufficient extent and duration to remove all other variables and conclude conclusively that any complex food is good or bad for us (and all natural foods are complex). Science is just not up to the job – not to mention the pressure it's often put under from commercial lobby groups – and most studies are inconclusive. It took thirty years to prove smoking kills, and that's a relatively simple case. Many of us, then, will continue to follow common sense and intuitive judgement that a diet grown with a little respect for nature is liable to be better for us and for the planet.

> *"There is little, if any, nutritional difference between organic and conventionally produced food", so says the FSA. More accurately, the most that could be claimed is that it cannot be proven with more than 95 per cent certainty that there are no differences.*

the three rules of flavour

A few years ago we tested every willing staff member for the sensitivity of their palate. The best formed a taste panel to assess the flavour of everything we grew; a good idea but, like so much science, it failed to deal with subjectivity and was excessively reductionist, tending to favour sweetness over anything challenging or complex. If we followed the panel's guidance we would never have sold a radicchio, endive or cardoon – a tragedy, in my opinion.

More recently, we've put together another in-house group of chefs and food enthusiasts to assess our carrots, cheese, wine and olive oil. Last week we sat down to taste the tomatoes from our tunnels; as always, our cherry tomato, *Sakura*, won, along with some new-trial yellow baby plum tomatoes. In spite of the subjectivity of taste, there is a general consensus that great flavour comes from a combination of three things:

Variety
The more you intensively select for yield or early maturity, the more you lose less easily quantified traits like complex flavours and nutritional value. Over thirty years I've seen many of the varieties we had selected for flavour dropped from breeders' lists because they're deemed less commercial. Consolidation in the seed trade just adds to this – after a global buying spree the multinational agribusiness Monsanto* now owns a staggering 23 per cent of the global seed trade and is negotiating to buy Syngenta who own a further 9 per cent.

Growing conditions

Up to a point, slow, steady growth from a healthy, well-balanced soil creates the best flavour. Excessive water and soluble nitrogen gives the luxuriant growth and high yields which look great in the field but disappoint in the kitchen. On the other hand, too much stress can result in excessive bitterness, toughness and 'off' flavours, particularly in the brassica family – though in carrots and some herbs drought can result in incredible flavour.

Harvest freshness and post-harvest storage

Ideally, fruit should be harvested fully ripe and never see a cold room, while green veg should be picked with the dew on them and eaten as soon as possible. Refrigeration can greatly extend life, but with variable impact on flavour: fine for salads, not great for courgettes. We try to maximise taste by respecting the likes and dislikes of every kind of fruit and veg.

In spite of these three rules, dealing with veg is like dealing with people – you won't get the best out of them if you treat them all in the same way. Farming is not a one-rule-fits-all business.

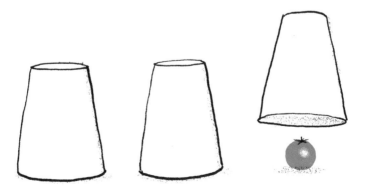

how much choice do we need?

We are enjoying a bumper crop of excellent runner and French beans, succulent sweetcorn and some of the best carrots I've tasted in thirty years. 2016 is turning out to be a good summer for most crops. About 90 per cent of your box contents are meticulously planned a year or more ahead, but yields and maturity dates vary, creating gluts and shortages. Inevitably we deviate from our 'ideal' contents to accommodate these variations up to a point – although exactly where that point is we argue about a lot. It's a compromise between keeping you happy in the kitchen and at the table on one hand, and avoiding waste and supporting committed growers on the other.

One of the things that I am most proud of about Riverford is that while we are not perfect, we are good to our word; if we agree to buy a crop from a grower and it meets our quality criteria (where the emphasis is on flavour, not appearance), we take 100 per cent of the agreed tonnage and pay 100 per cent of the agreed price. This is a remarkable achievement in an industry where a third of farmers' crops are regularly left in the field, and growers are expected to sell their souls along with their crops to keep buyers happy and shelves full.

How do we manage it? In part because, as farmers ourselves, we understand the realities of growing veg; partly because we invest heavily in long-term relationships with growers and don't have a buyer's tantrum at the first sign of an imperfect cabbage leaf; and in part because of meticulous planning. But a lot is down to how your trust as customers allows us to tweak the veg box contents to keep both growers and cooks happy, avoid waste and so create the value that means our veg is usually 20 per cent cheaper than supermarket organic veg. It's a partnership, and mostly it works incredibly well.

Choice, flexibility and convenience (arguably not our strong points) come at a price that the consumer seldom sees. It is paid by the fulfilment-centre worker and by the delivery driver, both earning less than the living wage; by the farmer whose crop is left unsold; by the environment as vans chase delivery slots, crop surpluses rot in fields and airplanes fly freight to achieve quick turnarounds. All of that sacrifice to give us endless choice. Frustrating when much of the time, I for one, don't really know what I truly want anyway.

autumn plenty

The sun is sinking but the soil is still warm
and active, feeding bumper crops. Mellow
fruitfulness or gluts and hectic abundance.
Pumpkins and squash ripen, sweetcorn
abounds. Harvesters sift roots from the soil
and laden trailers haul nuggets to store. It's
a struggle to pick, cook and eat it all – time
for squirrels and homely souls to dry, pickle,
ferment and make jam enough to see them
through the winter. By the time the first
frost slows things down, we're grateful
to ease into our winter routine.

smith, stalin – or a third way?

We love September. Planting and weeding are over, bar a few beans, garlic and onions, and we settle into the less stressful routine of harvesting the fruits of our labours. However, no sooner have we finished planting than it is time to start planning next year's veg boxes. Every year is different and we have to respond to weather variations. I'm convinced the effort we put into this is vital to the success of Riverford.

Traditionally, September was a time of gluts, when markets were flooded and crops wasted in the fields ("bean time is lean time" is the saying in the veg trade). Thanks to the box scheme and meticulous planning, we find a home for every cabbage, lettuce and tomato, even in a good growing year like this one.

According to eighteenth-century economist Adam Smith, a multitude of growers competing with each other in a perfect global market should drive innovation and guide resources towards the most efficient systems of production and distribution.

When I started growing veg I was appalled by the waste this generates. There are few things more depressing than a wholesale market on an autumn Saturday morning. Worse still is the waste of skill and investment, and the individual suffering that results from constant, short-term response to market forces.

Stalin thought he could do better with farm collectives, central-state control and five-year plans – the ensuing starvation and mass graves suggest not. History shows that ideological dogma can be even more brutal than Smithian economics.

As in so many areas of life, moderation would seem to be the answer. We put a huge amount of effort into planning production and invest heavily in nurturing long-term relationships with our growers, but I think we are a bit more pragmatic and flexible than Stalin. We are mindful of Adam Smith's lessons about the harshness of the marketplace; working to reduce waste and cost is one thing, but the challenge is to combine it with running a healthy business. I am determined to keep looking for better ways – and the cheapness of our boxes compared to supermarket organic veg suggests that we are going in the right direction.

the art of box packing

People who visit the farm expecting to see a bunch of laconic, grass-chewing Worzel Gummidges are often surprised by the frenetic activity and level of organisation. Sometimes, on my more objective days, I wonder at how thirteen farms, over a hundred people, numerous tractors, vans and mobile phones come together to produce your boxes each day.

The picking crew often starts at six to ensure there are sufficient stocks for the packers to start by eight thirty. By eleven the first orders are being collated, ready to be loaded after lunch. If any one item is late getting back to the barn, the whole process grinds to a halt and your box might arrive late. It is amazing how rarely this happens, and if it does, how quickly a solution is found.

It would be relatively easy to organise, if it were not for the innate perishability and variability of most vegetables, and the fact that we grow over eighty crops, compared to most farmers' five to ten. The potential for mistakes is almost infinite – and terrifying to contemplate. On the mornings when I stray from my office and roll my sleeves up, I am staggered by how it all comes together ready for the lorries and vans to roll out at the end of the day as the last of the staff fill out their time sheets and head home.

The business with all its interactions of people, nature and machines is an ongoing creative endeavour. It is like a three-dimensional jigsaw where the pieces keep changing shape – or like the pieces of sculpture that I used to make, but got bored of before they were finished. Riverford keeps evolving, so I will never be bored and it will never be finished. Some might think me mad or pretentious, but on those objective days I can even find an abstract beauty amongst the frenetic activity.

the *f* word & togetherness

Twenty years ago my evenings were spent chugging around south Devon in a beaten up Transit van, delivering to our early vegbox customers. Our offering was pretty basic but the reception was rapturous and we never looked back. It certainly beat being abused by supermarket buyers. As customer numbers grew, I bought more clapped-out vans, employed wayward drivers, and started getting complaints about service, bruised veg and bad driving. It made sense to contract out the delivering and go back to what I loved and was good at: growing the veg. What started as a loose agreement with musicians and misfits with underutilised vans evolved into a franchise by the late '90s.

I never meant to get into franchising. For years no one could mention the f word; to me it meant bad burgers and a wired-back, 'have a nice day' smile. Most Riverford veg teams join because, like me, they love good food, believe in organic farming, good business and making the world a better place. We are totally dependent on each other and on the growers who supply us.

Last month we gathered at Sacrewell, our farm on the edge of the Fens, to share experiences and innovations, to plan, drink, eat and make merry. Since the recession hit in 2008 it has been harder to win and keep customers. A few franchisees left, but mostly we've collectively adjusted to a much harder market with a renewed determination to do better. The feeling of togetherness left me full of optimism for the future. Good business, like many good things in life, is all about nurturing long-term relationships. A sense of shared purpose and an innate desire to do things well are powerful motivators. In the early hours, outside a tent full of dancing franchisees, I felt happy that the f word could be good.

2ND SEPTEMBER 2013
eccentrics & earthworms

It is reassuring to find that Charles Darwin and I are not alone in our obsession with earthworms. There is Emma Sherlock from the Natural History Museum (endearingly bonkers) who travels the globe looking for new species; Rachel Lovell (mildly eccentric) who with Emma's expertise has organised Riverford's Big Worm Dig citizen science project; and the many of you who have rummaged in your gardens for our survey. It has been great to see children swiftly overcome their squeamishness, to find and identify worms while getting muddy in the process.

Why are we making so much fuss about these dumb, arguably dull (sorry Emma) workhorses of the underworld? Without them burying organic matter, and constantly mixing, aerating and draining the soil, life on this planet would be very hard for other species. Especially for farmers and even more for organic farmers. Without chemical fertilisers, we need an active soil which recycles nutrients efficiently; worms are the first stage of this process and a great indicator of the general health of the soil.

Yet, as with bees, we are slaughtering our allies with toxic agrochemicals and brutish farming techniques. Organic farming, with its absence of pesticides and scorching fertilisers, alongside better management of organic matter (worm food), is probably better, but it pains me to think of the carnage a plough or rotavator causes. Sadly, as with so many aspects of ecology, worms would be better off if we just went away. Maybe one day we will be smart enough to grow our food without such brutal interventions, but in the meantime, should I somehow find myself living the life of a worm, I'd chose an organic field any day.

our fragile soil

All good farmers and gardeners are obsessed with their soil. They will talk about how lively it is to walk over, how it feels when kneaded, how it smells, and on occasion even how it tastes. All these senses indicate whether it is 'in good heart'. A healthy soil is teaming with bacteria, fungi, insects, and, in particular, earthworms. These unseen, and largely unknown creatures, together with the crops we sow, make up a complex and delicate ecosystem. Like us, they all need oxygen, which diffuses down through the small spaces between the soil particles.

When it rains, the gaps between those particles get clogged with water - OK for a few days and a healthy soil will normally drain quickly to allow the air back in. The problems start when the farmer is impatient to harvest his carrots or potatoes. Tractors and even human feet on wet soil can cause enormous damage, quickly reducing a good field to a mud bath. This makes work miserable for the pickers and means that the natural soil structure and drainage is lost. The soil around gateways becomes airless and puddled like potters' clay – and eventually dies, acquiring a rank smell typical of anaerobic* bacteria. The only answer then is to sow a grass or clover ley and wait for nature to repair the damage.

Over the years we have built a variety of crazy, low-ground-pressure harvesting vehicles to protect our soils when harvesting. Our quandary this autumn is that most of our soils have been saturated for six weeks and we are now desperate to harvest the maincrop potatoes and carrots before the first hard frosts. Much as it hurts to damage our beloved soil, I think there will be some unhappy earthworms this year.

cider without rosie

Going back a generation or two, when most of the farms in our parish were owned by the Church of England, it was said that cider would pay the rent. Each farm was surrounded by orchards and would have its own mill, press and cellars for storing and maturing the cider. Every now and then someone will still knock on our door and recount their time as a GI or Land Girl, when cider could be bought from Mr. Hoare, the previous tenant.

Before the war, cider was popular and, as a cash crop, helped farmers in this parish to survive the Depression of the '30s in relative prosperity. After the war, it fell from favour and the presses and orchards started to crumble into disrepair. By the time my father took on the tenancy in the '50s, there were only two working presses left in the village. As children we used to make our pocket money by collecting the apples and delivering them to these remaining presses, where sour-smelling, foul-mouthed men in leather aprons would amuse themselves by plying us with last year's cider whilst the apples were tipped from hessian sacks and disappeared up a conveyor into the mill.

The orchards, which once covered a third of the farm, have been slowly grubbed out. But recently, just as the remains of the industry was going into its death throws, there has been a bit of a revival locally. My brother-in-law – founder of Luscombe Drinks – bought the last press in the village when it was finally ripped out to make way for more barn conversions. He has developed a thriving business, though juices, ginger beer and lemonade are now much more important than cider.

My brother Oliver has replanted some of the orchards on the farm using a mixture of heritage and more modern varieties. Devon is mainly known for cider apples rather than dessert fruit because the damp climate makes the less hardy dessert-apple trees susceptible to fungal diseases. The English apple season is now well under way. Most of our apples will come from Jerry Saunders at Dawlish and David Pardoe in Herefordshire. This month it will be mainly Lambournes, Spartans and George Ross before we get into the Coxes at the end of the month. The better-keeping Russet, Kids Orange and Red Pippin should keep us in English apples well into the New Year.

pragmatism & beans from the vendée

Despite the nation's newfound enthusiasm for local produce, few of us relish the limitations of a dogmatically local diet. The last two miserable growing seasons have again highlighted the vegetable-growing limitations of our climate. Our challenge is to produce interesting boxes for customers all year round with minimal environmental impact and maximum benefit to our growers. This involves a pragmatic and considered compromise.

That local is not always best for the environment is clear from our studies with Exeter University; growing in heated glasshouses, for example, is environmental insanity. Veg not grown in the UK currently comes largely from southern Spain – a 24-hour lorry journey emitting 200-300g of CO_2 per kilo of produce. Years of poring over climatic maps of Europe and of visiting foreign growers have convinced me of a better alternative. The coastal area of France between La Rochelle and Nantes (the Vendée) enjoys very high levels of sunlight, mild winters, plenty of water for irrigation and pockets of good quality land – a vegetable grower's paradise, in fact. Produce picked one day could cross the Channel overnight and be in the boxes the next day with emissions of around 47g of CO_2 per kilo.

After twenty-five years of milking cows and keeping chickens, Didier, Brigitte and Mouilleau had worried long enough about the bank loans and wanted out. We have become firm friends in the months spent wading through French bureaucracy to finalise our purchase of their farm. When Didier came to Devon to check whether we were the sort of farmers who would look after his farm properly, he was so impressed that he has decided to stay on as a partner; maybe farming could be fun after all. So in this new venture Didier and Brigitte will look after the animals and the fertility-building pastures; Gary, a French-speaking, globe-trotting agronomist will organise the vegetable-growing; and Riverford will use the produce in your boxes.

The area is famous for its beans, its ducks and its 'mâche' (lamb's lettuce) and everything develops four to six weeks earlier than on our Devon farm. The land will become fully organic in 2009, when we will grow early salads, sweetcorn, spinach and beans outside, as well as tomatoes, cucumbers and peppers under cover. We are planning a campsite beside the irrigation lake so you can visit us. Far from resenting us as English invaders, the local farming community has been very welcoming and encouraging. I hope you, too, will welcome this as a sensible compromise, consistent with our values and will enjoy the new source of Riverford produce.

10TH SEPTEMBER 2001
happy birthday

Yesterday was, somewhat arbitrarily, selected as the tenth
birthday of the 'vegetable box scheme' by the Soil Association*.
Fittingly the celebrations were held where it all started – at the
Deans' farm near Exeter – with media, champagne and celebrity
chefs. Who would ever have thought it?

Our own scheme, which was originally closely modelled
on the Deans', is now eight years old. Over a fantastic lunch,
Jan Dean reminded me of my initial scepticism. Overcoming
my doubts and vowing to break away from the boa-constrictor
embrace of the supermarkets, I started with just thirty boxes,
packed in old orange crates and delivered from the back of my
battered Citroën 2CV. Feedback from customers was immediate
and positive, which has always been one of the joys of the scheme.
Over the years the quality and variety of our vegetables has
improved enormously as a result of that feedback.

The scheme became so successful that we encouraged
our neighbours to convert to organic farming. Nine disparate
farmers met in a pub and subsequently came together to form
South Devon Organic Producers* with the aim of growing
and selling organic vegetables as part of a balanced rotation
on mixed, family farms. Seven were not even organic at the
time and only two had any experience of growing vegetables.
We had no machinery, no premises, no staff and perhaps most
significantly, no experience of running a co-op. Looking back
it really was foolhardy even to try but somehow we pulled it off.

We now make over 4,000 boxes a week. We have all increased our production and we have more farmers wanting to join. Successful co-ops are thin on the ground and people travel from around the world to hear how we managed it. Apart from keeping some small family farms in business, the best things about the co-op is the mutual support, security and even fun that it has brought to an industry that is for the most part in relentless decline.

organic integrity

Considering that organic farming represents less than 2 per cent of the overall market, it accounts for an astonishing amount of food-related media coverage. Over the last fifteen years that coverage has been overwhelmingly positive, sometimes unquestioningly and almost embarrassingly so, reflecting an idealised image of the small-scale, ethically-committed producer valiantly struggling to bring an earthy sanity to a mad world.

It is worth remembering that the rules governing organic production define a system of farming. They say nothing about how food is packaged, how fresh it is, how far it travels, at what scale it is produced, how fairly workers and farmers are treated or whether businesses are motivated by philosophical commitment or the more conventional profit motive. In deciding whether the food you buy is part of the problem or part of the solution, organicness is just one factor in a horribly complex equation.

The last fortnight has seen suggestions in the press and on Newsnight that organic standards are being watered down in response to commercial pressures resulting from growth in the organic market – and that the Soil Association* is responsible. This is categorically not the case. In my twenty years of organic farming, standards have been progressively tightened. The Soil Association, just one of several certifying bodies, has often been a lone voice lobbying to raise standards in the UK and Europe, particularly in the area of poultry. It is extraordinary to hear them being criticised for being too lax when they have been so resistant to pressure, mainly from larger, new producers, to bend to commercial demands.

Terry Leahy, boss of Tesco, last week suggested that his well-intentioned institution could not source enough UK product to satisfy its recent appetite for UK organic because producers were "not professional". He might do well to speak with his buyers who put so many UK producers out of business while they scour the world for the cheapest organic produce produced to the lowest standards. The real pressure on the integrity of organic farming comes from the large, supermarket compliant producers, many of whom were forced into organic production by fear of losing conventional* business unless they danced to the supermarket buyer's tune. They may share the same organic symbol but on the broader issues they are the antithesis of those philosophically motivated organic pioneers who have populated the newspapers and developed the market that the new entrants want to exploit.

keeping things good & simple

Gordon Ramsay said that "he knew it would be good, but not that good". Now Bob Granleese in the Guardian Restaurant Guide has given Riverford's Field Kitchen nine out of ten. We would have scored ten, but for our "insipid" coffee (harsh but sadly true – we're working on it). Best of all was his amazement at the price. By having a set menu, keeping things simple and using predominantly our own ingredients, we have found a way of serving inspiring food at a price accessible to all. It is my job to be the miserable git who focuses on the missing one mark out of ten – how to improve the coffee, but the Field Kitchen really has grown into something I am very proud of.

Ethics and corporate responsibility have got the boardrooms of the country all in a dither. Accountants and marketeers are struggling to fit these imponderables into a version of the world where everything is measured and totted up in the same column with £s the only accepted units. With this comes a flood of conferences and speaking invitations to the freaks from the fringes; I am never sure whether to welcome mainstream interest. Will our ideas be adopted or corrupted? I hate the concept of an ethical market and resent businesses using ethics as a means of differentiation, and, by implication, exclusion, usually on the basis of price.

Making good food affordable to all is central to what we do, and we have always fought against the tendency for organic food, and box schemes in particular, to become the latest defining element of our bizarre class system. As with the Field Kitchen, by keeping things simple and limiting choice, we have kept the costs down, so that at most times of year our larger boxes are cheaper than equivalent non-organic vegetables from a supermarket. Very few ethical issues offer black and white answers. Decisions always rely on subjective assessments of the relative importance of different, often conflicting issues. The problem with the concept of an ethical market is that it always begs the question: whose ethics?

With only a month before we can expect our first frost it would take a miracle to ripen our pathetic butternut squash crop; it looks like being a complete failure. The squash in the boxes this week are from Spain – a travesty for a box scheme and certainly in conflict with our ethics, but there is nothing in the UK to replace them and they taste far better than ours ever do.

negotiating customer taste...

First, thanks to all of you who responded to the straw poll posing the question of 'English, in-conversion apples versus Italian, fully-organic ones' once the UK supply of organic ones has been exhausted. The huge majority (over 95 per cent) were in favour of supporting Paul Ward in Kent through the conversion period. I find it very frustrating having to use so much imported fruit and have always been happy to acknowledge that life is more complicated than simply 'organic is best'. We are still mulling over the labelling and logistical issues, but we may possibly use them from December. (Rest assure that everything else we sell is, and will continue to be, fully organic – and that we will never sell airfreighted produce).

Though I am delighted to find we are so aligned with you on apples, there is some divergence over cabbages and beetroot. There have been quite a few Hispi cabbages in the boxes over the summer and we are just starting to get a trickle of moans. These one-meal cabbages are so sweet to eat and easy to prepare that, rather than meekly backing down and ploughing them in, I feel moved to suggest that only a wuss can't eat two or three cabbages in a month! Eat them fresh – by the time the outer leaves are yellowing they will have lost their sweetness and best nutritional value.

As you may suspect, my enthusiasm is partly based on the ease with which they grow. But if we tried to fill the boxes with highly-strung, labour-intensive veg – beans, tomatoes, peppers and rocket – unless we charged a lot more, we wouldn't last long.

We all hate waste but, should your unloved cabbage end its life on the compost heap, it might be some consolation to know that, in financial terms, they constitute a relatively small part of the box.

On a less belligerent note, perhaps we did overdo it on the summer beetroot. I love them and, on the basis of their rise to fashion amongst cookery writers last year, thought the nation was with me. I should have known that anything causing that much bathroom trauma had limited appeal. A few less next year I think.

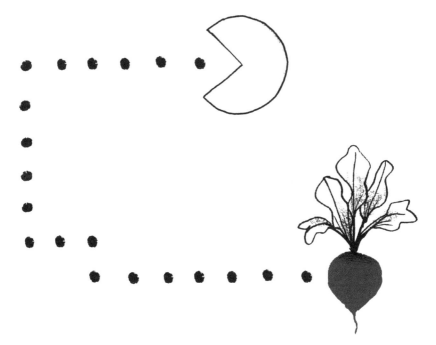

climbing the walls

A combination of cola and certain orange, processed foods make my youngest son quite uncontrollable. It can be entertaining for a few minutes, but I would hate to have to deal with him in a classroom. Mostly he is deprived of the junk he craves by his puritanical father, but I sometimes relent at the cinema with the result that he once had to be physically restrained in the aisle halfway through Lord of the Rings. The Food Standards Agency deserves some credit for sponsoring Southampton University to do the research that confirms beyond doubt what many parents and teachers have known for decades: certain additives in highly processed foods send certain children up the wall. Perhaps more disturbing is the finding that these foods can cause a "deterioration in behaviour in the general population".

How can it be OK to knowingly feed our children unnecessary colourings and preservatives that radically alter their behaviour? How can we be expected to trust our government and its regulating authority, the FSA, when, after consultation with the food and drink industry but no one else, it refuses to act on its own research? Why has it taken thirty years for science to 'prove' what many parents know from their own living experiment of raising children? Isn't it an abdication of governmental responsibility to suggest that we make our judgements based on labels read by few and intelligible to even fewer?

Very few issues are so black and white and call so unambiguously for government action, NOW. It is all too reminiscent of tobacco and cancer, asbestos and asbestosis, BSE and CJD and more recently the continuing abuse of antibiotics in agriculture, the rise of MRSA and general antibiotic resistance. Commercial interests, protected by cynical PR and intense lobbying, have built expertise at delaying legislative action so that a profit stream can be maintained for a few more years. There is no doubt that these additives will be banned but when the evidence is so clear why does it have to be such an uphill battle, subject to delay at every turn? The FSA was set up after a collapse in public confidence in the old Ministry of Agriculture, Fisheries and Food after BSE. It was supposed to be independent of commercial interests. The problem seems to be that the name might have changed but the spinelessness of the bureaucrats hasn't.

potato special

A few years ago a fibre optic cable was being laid across the farm. The trenching crew were mainly Irish and moved with great efficiency, until they came to a small patch of potatoes in one of our fields. The crop was nearing maturity and it would surely be sacrilegious to waste them. No amount of piece-work incentives could get the digger bucket into the ground. Though we had struck a deal where we were paid for the potatoes they destroyed, work came to a halt while a harvester was fetched and a strip-cleared ahead of their machines.

I love to see the harvester gently lift a ridge of potatoes and to watch as the fine soil falls away, leaving the nugget-like tubers on the harvester's web, on their way to the trailer and the barn. All the potatoes, bar eight acres of reds, are safely in the barn now, stored in one-ton wooden boxes. After a few weeks of circulating ambient air to dry and cure the skins, we will reduce the temperature to three or four degrees centigrade and maintain a fairly high humidity. In effect, we are mimicking the tubers' natural conditions in the soil – but without the slugs, wireworms* and frost. If we get it right the later varieties will keep in perfect condition through to next May, when we start harvesting the new crop.

The potato is one of the heroes of our veg boxes and we grow over twenty varieties to suit the different seasons, soil types and to give a range of flavours and textures. Resistance to the dreaded potato blight is also a major factor. Non-organic potatoes will normally be sprayed with a fungicide every seven to ten days.

This year's crop has been harvested at the right time, in perfect conditions and should store well as a result. I had been dreading a repeat of last year, when a dry end to the summer produced tubers with exceptionally high dry matter, which then bruised at harvest even if handled as gently as eggs. The cows ended up eating almost as many as we sold. I think they will have to eat grass this year.

YOU TUBER

disillusioned with uniformity in my artichokes

Last week I was singing the praises of hybrids, with just a few reservations. In the space of one damp week the first hybrid variety of my beloved artichokes succumbed to mildew and is now all but dead; what promised to be a bumper yield ended up barely paying for the inflated cost of the seed (four times the price of non-hybrids). Next door, in the genetically highly varied, open pollinated* variety, a few plants have been weakened but most have the genetics to resist the pathogen* and are still doing well.

Hybrids can produce high yields and be uniform in appearance and maturity, making them quick to pick; but their narrow genetic base means they are often poorly equipped to withstand the challenges of pest and disease attack, weather extremes or areas of low fertility in the field. Farmers become enslaved to meeting the narrow needs of their hybrid seeds, whatever the environmental cost. Farmers and customers have come to expect, and even require, the uniform vegetables that hybrids produce, to the extent that it is getting harder and harder to find a market for the traditional open pollinated varieties which often look wild and woolly by comparison. Were we always drawn to that controlled, neat uniformity or have our eyes been trained to it by the environment we live in, and more particularly shop in, with all those neat parallel shelves?

Uniformity is an anathema in nature; it is inherently unstable and risky. When the meteorite strikes, the volcano erupts or the glaciers melt it is the freaks on the fringes that provide the genetic diversity that allows adaptation and survival. The uniform mainstream, specialised to narrow 'normality', is wiped out when normality shifts. Given the current market paradigm, it is hard to argue against the development of narrow normality as represented by hybrids (and GM* in more extreme circumstances), but it will be wiped out; maybe not in my lifetime and maybe not by this freak, but it will happen. One day earthlings will look back on the lumbering and domineering Monsanto* and Tesco with the dismay and disbelief elicited when looking up at T. rex in the Natural History Museum.

to autumn

Autumn newsletters seldom escape some reference to mists and
mellow fruitfulness. In two hundred years no one has evoked
a grower's September satisfaction better than Keats in the first
verse of 'To Autumn'. As a philistine farmer I never get beyond
the first line, but such is the diversity of our workforce that on
a particularly beautiful autumn morning while harvesting a
particularly bountiful crop of squash, we were treated to a perfect
rendition of all three verses by an otherwise subdued field worker.
It was many years ago and I can't remember his name, but I can
remember exactly where I was in that field on top of a hill looking
down on the clearing mist in the valley, as well as the satisfying
weight of the gourds and a feeling of overwhelming harmony
and wellbeing.

Like many growers, I love autumn; when we reap the rewards
of summer's work, when the dews last longer, the sun is gentle and
things slow down, affording a chance to savour. After a miserable
July and August, the dry, sunny weather we have enjoyed recently
is particularly welcome. The bounty is spectacular, almost worrying:
leeks, corn, cabbages, broccoli, carrots, potatoes, beans, spinach
and chard are rolling in by the trailer load – to the extent that for
the first time ever we are planning to export some surplus to a
box scheme in Dorset. Mercifully, as the days shorten and night
temperatures drop, growth is slowing down so I am pretty
confident it will all find space on a plate somewhere.

pumpkin day

With the first hard frosts expected soon I am glad to see all our squash and pumpkins safe in the barns. For ten years we have opened the farm on the last Saturday before Halloween and sold our pumpkin crop with the proceeds going to Oxfam. This year we will be open on Saturday, 30th October for box customers and the public to come and choose their pumpkin. There will be guided walks, tractor and trailer tours, apple pressing and lunch served in our new Field Kitchen. I prefer to think of the day as a harvest festival more than for remembering the dead and their restless souls.

Ian Samuel, our co-op's carrot specialist, was recently at a carrot-variety trial with a bunch of farmers and found that he was the only one tasting carrots. All the other farmers were trying to break them on their wellies. The reason is that the most important criteria for a commercial carrot variety is resistance to breakage so that it can be harvested, tipped, poured, washed, and now even polished, all mechanically and without breakage. The most popular variety, Nairobi, which accounts for 70 per cent of all supermarket carrots, can be dropped out of an airplane without breaking. In all the taste trials we have done it consistently comes at the bottom and we never grow it. All our carrot varieties are selected primarily for their flavour and secondarily for disease resistance, yield and the wellie test.

who owns those potatoes & does it matter?

Last time I met Keith Abel (founder of Abel & Cole, Riverford's arch rival), he told me over a pork pie, "The problem with you, Guy, is that you're so f . . . ing boring". He looked pretty pleased with life and I wondered if he was right.

We started our businesses about the same time. He was selling potatoes door to door; I was growing them. We both ended up selling vegetable boxes. I reckon ours are better, but he has always been better at selling them and making money out of it. After twenty years, with impeccable timing, Keith sold his creation to a venture capitalist backed by Lloyds Bank and bought an estate in the country. But within two years, without Keith's vision, the business was struggling. The venture capitalists left, Lloyds took control and Keith was brought back to save the day, which he seems to have done very successfully. Last week William Jackson, a food group with no history in organic or home delivery, bought the business from Lloyds for an undisclosed sum.

At the time of the original sale I was besieged by accountants, lawyers and merchant bankers, all claiming they were perfectly placed to maximise the value of my business and ease me into a life of champagne-swilling happiness. I refused to let Riverford be milked dry by greedy cynics who saw it only as a cash cow; nothing would please me more than to show there was a better way.

Prompted by an awareness of my own mortality, and an admiration for the John Lewis Partnership, I spent a couple of years visiting co-ops and researching employee ownership. I later got excited about another alternative: persuading all of you (our customers) to buy Riverford, converting us into a customer-owned co-operative. The lumbering complexity and looks of incomprehension when I tried to explain it put me off that plan, though I have not quite given up. When I am too decrepit to be any use, my stab at immortality is to devise a form of ownership for the benefit of all those involved: staff, customers and suppliers or perhaps a combination of all three. I just haven't quite worked out how to do it yet.

progress comes from the periphery

This weekend I should be in Rome, speaking at an international agribusiness conference organised by the Harvard Business School. Or should I? The big guns from Monsanto*, Unilever and a host of other multinationals will be there, trying to figure out how to maintain or increase their hegemony over what the world eats and how it is produced.

There is an evolutionary theory that suggests progress happens at the fringes. Species or races scratching an existence on the margins are the ones that thrive and become dominant when a change in the environment means the centre-dwelling giants' necks are too big or their legs too short. The same is true of business; the giants in the centre find it hard to adapt, are inward-looking and have no incentive to be original. Things change (most notably consumers' opinions) and they tend to be too cumbersome and self-congratulatory to realise that the traits that brought success will soon bring extinction. Many recognise their limitations and go hunting for ideas either by gobbling up small companies, complete with brands and ideas, or by going to conferences and listening to the freaks from the fringes.

I was invited to present a paper on Riverford and I am sure it would have been a fascinating experience and a real insight into some of the forces that shape our world. A wise aunt, on hearing one of my rants against Monsanto during our 1998 GM* court case, used to counsel me not to demonise my opponents but rather to seek to understand them. In the end, though, I was put off by the bumf about the conference, which brought home just how wide the gulf was between my approach to food, farming and business and theirs. I don't have much interest in building bridges to help them make more money; I would rather spend the weekend with my family.

It is a shame that so many of the cleverest people end up working for these companies, thereby giving them the intellectual power to subsume all in their path. The box scheme, and our way of connecting farmers with food-lovers, is something that I feel inclined to protect jealously. Unlike Green & Blacks, Rachel's Organic and numerous other pioneers in the organic market, I will never sell out. I am also acutely aware of the need to protect what we have created and resist the insidious, creeping compromises that mainstream business practices try to impose on the people with principled ideas.

cheap food, dignity & victorian working practices

Our Polish worker Martin arrived twenty years ago with a tent and a guitar. He came back the following summer with some friends, and the farm has become increasingly dependent on Eastern European workers ever since. I am frequently asked how we will cope post-Brexit if there are no new migrants; the answer is, it will be tough, but not impossible. There will be lots of restructuring in food and farming, bringing opportunities for new entrants and smaller, more human-scale businesses; something I welcome. The relentless march to scale, whether on fruit farms of in poultry slaughterhouses, has been facilitated by the availability of compliant 'operatives' who don't question or complain and are therefore deemed to be happy. They are not; they have the same human needs for decent housing, dignity and respect as the rest of us, but simply have fewer options. Cheap food has too often come at the cost of a return to Victorian working practices. There are exceptions, but it has been too easy to be a bad employer in an industry I sometimes feel ashamed to be part of.

Today non-UK employees, mostly Romanian, Polish, Lithuanian and Slovakian, make up around 33 per cent of our staff (the norm in horticulture is closer to 90 per cent); they have made a huge contribution. Most started as seasonal field workers, and the majority return home after a season or two, while some have married, put down roots and worked their way up through the business.

Field work is unbelievably tough for those who have not experienced it. Hours in the gym will no prepare you for the endurance required; it takes at least a month for a fit and able body to become field-hardened. I used to do sixty hours a week, but I couldn't hack it now. It is a good guiding principle to avoid asking others to do what you wouldn't do yourself. While the commonly heard farmers' bleat that "Brits just don't want the work" is largely true, they should spend more time asking themselves why and what they could do to make the jobs more attractive. I for one will not be lobbying the government for agriculture to be a 'special case'; I almost relish the challenge of attracting and retaining staff in a post-Brexit UK. It will force us to do things we probably should be doing anyway.

war on waste

So Hugh Fearnley-Whittingstall has gone into battle again, this time with his 'War on Waste' programme on BBC One. The supermarkets' produce specifications, trading practices and spin come off badly, with the focus on Morrisons' demand for perfect parsnips. Hugh managed to find a rarity – a supermarket-supplying farmer who was willing to speak out. In this farmer's case as in most, work with supermarkets led to the extinction of the family business.

My own trading with supermarkets came to an end shortly after I was told my Little Gem lettuces would be on offer and I would be paid 6p per lettuce instead of 15p, the minimum we could live with. I left the office, picked up a sledgehammer and set about destroying the packhouse I had started building. Most growers get so ground down by this standard treatment that they suck it up until they go bust or get bought out in the never-ending consolidation of supply. Supermarkets just don't want to trade with small family businesses.

In my experience, the abuse that spews from a dissatisfied supermarket buyer makes Cruella de Vil seem like the Dalai Lama. No-one should treat another human being like that. Frustratingly, their petulant demands don't even reflect customer preferences. As Hugh points out and our customers tell us, most people don't expect vegetables to look like they were made in a factory. Yet natural variation is driven out when you supply a supermarket – creating staggering, unjustifiable waste.

Nothing makes me happier than leaving a field with just stumps standing after harvest, knowing we've sold every last cauliflower, lettuce or leek. We can only do that by having much more forgiving cosmetic specifications. At times I know we test your tolerance with gluts of broad beans or artichokes, but our assumption is that you're with us to feel connected with the people who grow your food, and that flavour and a sane food chain are what count. The whole system only works if we have the courage to risk irritating you now and then. If seven going on eleven billion of us are to share this planet, no-one can have exactly what they want all the time, not even a supermarket buyer.

organic energy

There are many good reasons for supporting organic agriculture. Some, like flavour, nutritional value and avoiding pesticides and additives in our diet, are essentially selfish. Some are more altruistic, like protecting biodiversity, animal welfare and reducing pollution. In the wake of the Stern Report, perhaps the best and most incontrovertible reason is that organic food requires an average of roughly half the energy to produce compared to non-organic agriculture. I say 'average' because there is a large range: from organic tomatoes produced out of season under heated glass (which is hugely inefficient in energy usage), to ruminant livestock (cows and sheep) eating organic grass, grown without fertiliser, which is many times more efficient than intensive systems using nitrogen fertiliser.

The cause of these differences is almost entirely attributable to the energy required to make nitrogen fertiliser. The air we breathe is 8 per cent nitrogen but it is in the form of a very stable N_2 molecule, which most plants cannot access. 37 per cent of the energy used in conventional* agriculture is used burning fossil fuels in the Haber process, to separate those two nitrogen atoms and convert them to ammonium nitrate, which can be absorbed by plants. Organic farmers instead rely on legumes (clover, peas, beans, vetches) that, by virtue of a symbiotic relationship with an agro-bacterium living in their roots, are able to harness the sun's energy to 'fix' atmospheric nitrogen. We typically grow two to four years of clover to build up fertility and feed grazing livestock, followed by two years of vegetables which are fed by the soil bacteria and fungi which recycle and release the nutrients held in the clover.

In addition to the energy consumed, the manufacture and use of nitrogen fertiliser also releases 80,000 tonnes of nitrous oxide (N2O) which is 300 times more potent as a greenhouse gas than carbon dioxide. By eating organic food, especially if grown locally and in season, you are taking one small step to save the planet. Of course, we still need to do a lot more.

Stern's main conclusion is that the benefit of strong, early action on climate change far outweighs the cost of that action.

Emissions of methane and nitrous oxides from livestock (and their manure) have more recently proved to be important in climate change as well – probably more important than nitrogen fertiliser.

AMMONIUM NITRATE

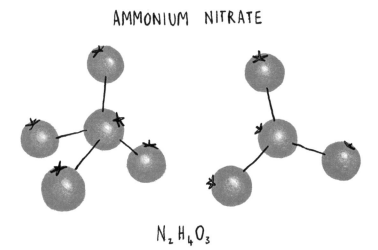

$N_2H_4O_3$

looks aren't everything

Sainsbury's have been born again as crusaders for ugly veg, valiantly fighting EU grading regulations to give us all those misshapen vegetables they have spent the last thirty years telling suppliers that customers don't want. Tesco meanwhile have gone ominously quiet about local sourcing (their 2007 enthusiasm), and have been reducing shelf space given to organic vegetables (passion of 2006) to make space for more bargain lines competing with the new threat of discounters Lidl and Aldi.

In the meantime, you may wonder what has happened to the farmers who were growing the cosmetically-perfect veg, the local courgettes, the organic potatoes. And remember those organic veg boxes fleetingly offered by Sainsbury's, Tesco and M&S? Land was converted to organic, packhouses commissioned and staff employed to support them. Where are they now?

While supermarkets pride themselves on giving us consumers what we want and responding to the latest trend, growers just can't keep up. It's not (just) that we are slow-witted, straw-chewing yokels; it takes a minimum of three years to go from producing fungicide-doused potatoes to growing organic ones. All businesses must evolve to survive and this includes farmers, but the pace of change must respect the restraints of nature and honour commitments to suppliers as well as customers. The farmer who grew the cauliflowers in your boxes in recent weeks (apologies that they have been small, the result of a poor growing season), has a barn full of cosmetically-perfect salad potatoes. Twelve months ago, when a particular supermarket wanted to be the greenest rather than the cheapest, he was persuaded to grow a substantial area of this particular variety organically. Now the supermarket doesn't want them because the shelf space has been given to cost-cutting lines. Add this to the worst growing year he has experienced and this farmer is facing ruin – one reason we will accept his small cauliflowers. We would like to use the spuds, but he was persuaded to grow a variety which looks good but has a nasty metallic aftertaste.

My point is that responsiveness comes at a cost, largely borne by suppliers and often invisible to customers. A sensible food policy (one that delivers healthy, tasty, affordable food at minimum environmental cost) will not emerge from fickle supermarket buyers chasing whimsical customers. It will take a bit of planning and a willingness to consider the unthinkable; that the customer cannot always have exactly what they want because the planet cannot afford it. It is my bet that most won't even miss it.

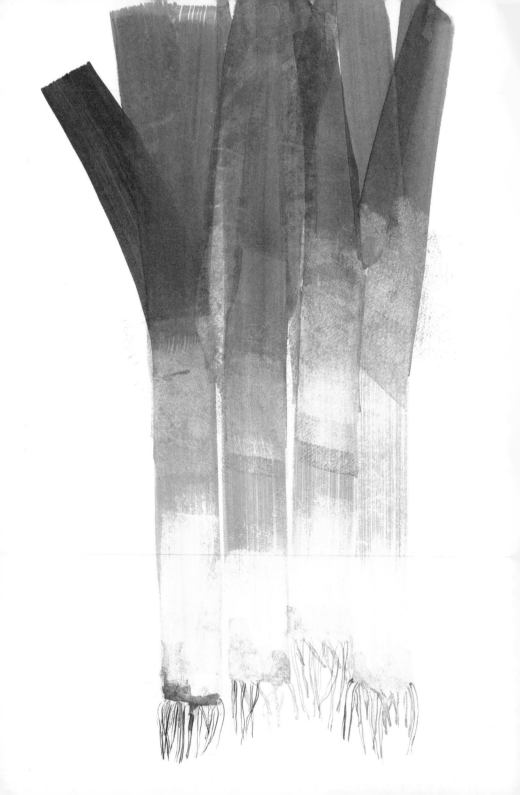

winter chill

Leeks, cabbage, caulifowers and kale.
Mud-laden boots and damp waterproofs.
In Devon, with the Atlantic on both sides,
it is often more winter sog and mud than
frozen chill. A time to eat roasts and
stew, read seed catalogues, plan and
fantasise about how much better
it will all be next year.

organic battles & celebrity tweets

When I established our co-operative of organic farmers in 1997, it took all my persuasive efforts and bullish determination to convince the nine co-founders to turn their backs on agrichemicals. Although we made mistakes along the way, it's hugely satisfying now to see their farms (many of which would not have been viable without the co-op) thriving and reinvesting in the future. The soils are healthier and their livestock happier, wildlife has flourished and the veg tastes pretty good as well. I think they have come around to the idea that organic is not so bad.

Five or six years ago, whatever the problem with the environment or our food, organic farming was held up as the answer in an almost embarrassingly unquestioning way. I am sure it was infuriating for those promoting, profiting from, and excited by chemical farming and genetic engineering and it was inevitable that they would fight back. For years various right-wing and mostly American think tanks (probably funded by GM* and agrichemical corporations) had been promoting anti-organic stories about mycotoxin* and bacterial contamination in organic food. They all turned out to be fabrications and they got little coverage for many years, but they kept chipping away. The tipping point in the UK came from the organic movement's intransigent objection to GM. This incensed many in the scientific community, particularly it would seem, Professor John Krebs (widely regarded as being pro-GM), who at the time headed up the Food Standards Agency. His extensively reported comments discredited and undermined organic farming and turned the tide; press on organic food has generally been negative ever since.

Which part of which scientific paper makes it into the headlines is enormously subjective and often determined by the story an editor is looking for. The underlying facts of organic farming haven't changed, but the organic market has declined by 20 per cent in the last two years, so it's clear that however fickle it may be, the media is a powerful thing. We've a glimmer of hope though, in the form of modern culture's latest darling, social media. An email came to us from Caggie Dunlop's office this week (she's from E4's 'Made in Chelsea' reality TV series – so outrageously bad, it's compulsive viewing). In return for free veg she's offered to tweet about us. But we've decided against it. I hope she doesn't turn into the next Professor Krebs.

The UK organic market bottomed out in 2011, growing again at between 4 and 9 per cent each year since. In 2015, a much larger EU-funded study was published which showed conclusively that there were significant differences in the nutritional value of organic food versus conventional* – almost always in favour of organic.

homage to a winter leek-picker

After a gloriously dry and bright autumn, winter arrived with a vengeance last weekend, stripping the last leaves from the trees and saturating our soil. Such rainfall can be hugely damaging in terms of soil erosion, but we were well-prepared: having loosened compacted tracks to aid rain penetration and mitigate flooding; added hardcore to muddy gateways and created some strategic dams. Tractors will now be banned from our lower-lying fields until spring to avoid destroying the delicate soil structure so critical to good crops next year. Winter harvesting of leeks, cabbage, kales and cauliflower will have to be done on foot, with the aid of tracked, low-ground-pressure vehicles.

It takes a very special person to withstand a winter in the fields. The physical hardship is not so much about the penetrating damp, but more the clawing mud hanging to your boots, making every step take twice the effort. Less sticky, sandy soils would make work easier, but as they can't hold moisture in summer or prevent nutrient run-off during the winter rains, they don't grow such good veg in organic systems. Our soils are mostly balanced, intermediate clay loams* with about 35 per cent clay.

We make sure our harvesting staff have good wet-weather gear, but a day in the driving rain pulling leeks must rank alongside fishing and coal mining as one of the toughest jobs on the planet. Many of our fields are too distant to get staff back to our canteen for lunch, so this winter we are experimenting with getting hot soup to them as a small gesture of appreciation. The individuals who stick at it year after year often acquire a Zen-like calm and say that even on the grimmest day they prefer being outside to working in the barns or office; I reckon it is genetic.

Other than genes, decent rain gear and hot soup, what makes a winter veg-picker happy is a good crop to get stuck into. Fiddling about trimming and sorting through undersized or diseased plants is frustrating in the summer but quickly becomes depressing in the winter. This year, however, after a good summer's growing, things are looking bright on this front for both our pickers and your boxes. Spare a thought for those hardy souls bent with their backs to the rain as you chop up your leeks; we would have no business and you no veg without them.

the root of the matter

It is still dry and bitterly cold. However, the sunshine has brought a noticeable lift to everyone's spirits. The beans and garlic have been sown in ideal conditions, but the dry weather came too late for the carrots; the tops had weakened so that too many snapped off as the harvesting machine eased them from the ground.

We were dreading going back to hand-harvesting the carrots but, with the ongoing dry weather, the potato harvester is doing a tolerable job. Instead of gripping the carrots by the leaves, this machine lifts the entire raised bed and sifts out the soil from the roots, which are then delivered to a trailer. Though this is standard practice on sand and peat soils in the East of England, with our more sticky loams* and higher rainfall, you tend to get more soil than carrot in the trailer in all but the driest of autumns. There will be plenty of sorting to do through the winter, but no one wanted to face the task of hand-harvesting and at least it is relatively warm sorting through veg in the barn.

How fresh are your roots? Not very, is the answer by April, but this should not bother you. I get a bit annoyed by veg 'experts' harping on about fresh roots when this has no meaning. The concept of freshness should be reserved for vegetables where it matters, particularly greens and soft fruit. Roots, bulbs and tubers are all nature's way of storing food in a dormant form from one growing season to the next. Over the millennia we have learnt to use this to keep our tables stocked through the winter.

What matters, in terms of the quality of roots, is not freshness, but how they are stored. Some, like parsnips and Jerusalem artichokes, can withstand the frost and are best left in the ground and lifted when needed. Potatoes, carrots and celeriac will be damaged by hard frosts and must be harvested in autumn and early winter for storage in a cool, damp, dark barn. The tradition was to build a clamp*, but after losing my first potato crop this way (they heated, grew sprouts and ended up as cow food), we have moved to storing in one-tonne, cold-stored bins. Carrots can be field-stored under the insulation afforded by lots of straw between two layers of plastic, but they taste better harvested in November and kept in barn storage until needed. Onions, like all bulbs, need to be cool and dry with a reasonable amount of ventilation.

bbc radio 4 farmer of the year

For many years I have been a big fan of Radio Four's food and farming programmes. Derek Cooper, who retired as presenter of The Food Programme a couple of years ago, is in my book up there with John Peel as one of the all-time greats of British broadcasting. This is why I was so thrilled to win the BBC Food and Farming 'Farmer of the Year' award last week.

The great thing about these awards is that they are initially based on the nomination of customers and then very carefully researched by experts in the industry. I should thank those many customers who nominated us. The judges, who each visited the farm for half a day, were Sir Don Curry (chairman of the post-foot-and-mouth-disease Curry Report, which is the basis of our government's current agricultural policy), Robert Clark (food retail analyst) and Steven Peacock from Radio Four. For all their charm they gave us a pretty good grilling, leaving few stones unturned – so I am all the more proud that we came through as the winner on Tuesday.

Meanwhile, back on the farm, we have finally given up on our onions. Having painstakingly graded through them and selected what seemed good for the following week's boxes, we were finding that by the time we packed the boxes half of them had gone bad. It was a hard decision, but we have given up, and the last thirty tonnes will be fed to our neighbours' cattle. Believe it or not, they go wild for them even if they are a little mouldy. For those of you who didn't complain, thanks for your patience and for those of you who did, thanks for taking the time to let us know. As this was a last-minute decision we had to buy some onions from Holland to fill the gap this week, but hope to find some from the UK in time for next week.

The barns are full to bursting with carrots, squash and potatoes. We have nearly run out of bins, crates and storage space because the carrots have produced such a bumper crop. The last harvest to be brought in will be the celeriac and beetroot. One small silver lining to the giant onion cloud is that at least we now have space to store these final crops before the first hard frosts can damage them. And they say that farmers do nothing but grumble...

In 2007 we took on a tenancy of a farm in Cambridgeshire with well-drained land and little more than half our rainfall. We have grown our onions there ever since with much more success than in damp Devon.

farming post-brexit: an industry at the crossroads

Two farming tribes gathered in Oxford last week: the mainstream Oxford Farming Conference, sponsored by pesticide and machinery suppliers and accountants; and – provocatively choosing the same two days – the Oxford Real Farming Conference. This is the radical challenger, with no suits or commercial sponsors; with more hair, more woolly jumpers, more women – and a lot of determination to change the direction UK farming has followed towards large-scale and intensification.

I spoke at both conferences, but felt more at home with the hair and jumpers. The suits were more open-minded than I expected though. They invited and listened to environmental journalist George Monbiot, who, with cool, well-informed and devastating logic, questioned the moral and political acceptability of paying three billion pounds to farmers in subsidies, with precious little in return. There seemed to be an acceptance that, post-Brexit, farmers will instead only be paid for what they deliver, whether it is food or 'public goods' (flood prevention, public access etc.).

Even more heartening was the acceptance that we cannot continue to abuse our soils, and better still that 'biological' farming offers a genuine alternative to blindly following the agrochemical and GM* industry.

Down the road at the Oxford Real Farming Conference, the feeling was of a movement that had found its time in history. There was talk of beliefs and justice, with an acceptance that, while farming decisions must not be based only on profit, profit was still vital. These were not the starry-eyed idealists that have sometimes driven me to distraction over the last thirty years; they were human and imaginative but above all, intensely practical in their search for ways to grow nutritious food with social and environmental justice. Like the fourteenth-century Peasants' Revolt and the seventeenth-century Diggers and Levellers, they lack the land, power and capital to match their determination and independence (and let's hope they don't get hanged this time). But in an industry depressingly subservient to the needs of its suppliers, these people bring hope and deserve support. Surely now, as the UK shapes its new, post-Brexit agricultural policy, it should look to serve the farmer, consumer and environment with equity and to support new entrants, rather than predominantly striving to perpetuate the privilege of the rich and powerful.

imperfection, sprouts & christmas banquets

Sprout harvesters will have been rumbling across the Fens night and day for the last fortnight, gobbling up rows of perfect sprouts, stripping them from the stalks, passing them through a cyclone, which sucks off the debris, before allowing the tight little buds to feed into a hopper. Unfortunately, such perfection requires the help of a barrage of sprays and, after the unchecked ravages of cabbage root fly, slugs, aphids and disease, the only way we can get acceptable sprouts is to pick them selectively, discarding the bad ones as we go.

Our Brussels sprouts are grown and hand-picked by Anthony and Mary Coker. Sprouts are one of the most difficult crops to grow organically and are one of the very few where I ask you to accept different cosmetic standards to those you would expect from a sprayed crop. We have saved the best of the bunch for this week, so that they can be left on the stalk – festively ornamental.

Last Saturday we went back to the barn where the business started eighteen years ago for our family Christmas party. My first memory of the barn is collecting eggs with my mother. Later the chickens (never a successful enterprise) gave way to cream teas served to tourists visiting the farm in the '70s. That was more profitable but far too stressful, so next it was a potter's studio before housing my potatoes, grader* and first office. In the late '80s, when the rave culture was outraging anyone too old to enjoy it, we allowed some friends to hold a Halloween party there. It got a bit out of hand, with the local constabulary setting up road blocks and subsequently threatening us with a £20,000 fine and three months in jail if we ever did it again. After that the barn did not see much action for a while.

A few years ago, realising that there was too much family to accommodate in his house for Christmas dinner, my brother welded a column of oil drums together to make a huge central chimney, roasting spit and fireplace and the barn became a banqueting hall. We have been using it for our Christmas parties ever since. The mingling odour of cow muck, souring milk and dairy detergent from outside adds savour to the food. Luckily, these days the only outrage comes from the cows next door.

courageous caulis & campaigners

It has been a wild, wet and windy couple of weeks since New Year and the ground is absolutely sodden. It is hard to imagine anything mustering enough enthusiasm to grow out there. Most of the crops take January off and will actually go backwards as they lose leaves to the gales, pigeons, rabbits and disease before lengthening days in February spur them into growth again.

Cauliflowers are the exception. It could be the full moon last week, or it could be the mildness of the wet weather, but there is nothing stopping them. The mid-winter varieties draw nutrients from their roots and stumps to produce their heads, rather than relying on photosynthesis, so they are able to grow curds* in near-darkness. Our battle-hardened cauli crew are out there in all weathers and are just about managing to keep up with the harvest. We are even exporting surplus to a box scheme in Denmark.

Last weekend I went to the Soil Association* annual conference. Jamie Oliver gave one of the worst talks I have ever heard and spent half the time plugging Sainsbury's, but I still couldn't help liking him. His message seemed to be that it was all about getting people enthusiastic about food and cooking, and that to do that you have to have good (real, organic) 'gear'. Food is so often a way of reinforcing all our worst class values. Jamie has a great talent for cutting through that by making cooking and the sharing of food fun and accessible.

The best talk, though, came from Michael Meacher, the environment minister who was sacked for caring too much about the environment. He drinks his morning tea out of a mug inscribed with the words, 'everyone has a right to my opinion'. Although determined and outspoken, he is actually very humble – a man with too much integrity to survive in politics. Apart from all the well-documented environmental benefits of organic farming, he quoted research that it also sequesters huge amounts of atmospheric carbon dioxide by increasing the levels of organic matter in the soil. Organic farming could be even more significant as a means of countering global warming than planting or maintaining forests.

make like a plant

Hurrah, the shortest day is past. Combined with some bright and dry weather, I feel better already. This will be our busiest week of the year as the nation prepares to feast on some good, wholesome, and for once, largely seasonal, food. Out in the fields you can almost feel the plants shutting down as the shorter days, a lower sun and sudden drop in temperature snuff out their last half-hearted attempts at late-autumnal growth. Plants and beasts pause before rushing on with 2010. Even in mild Devon, nothing much happens out there now until late January. It is a strange phenomenon that even in southern California or the south of Spain, where winter temperatures and light levels are similar to our summer, there is always a brief period when plants virtually shut down. Experienced growers seldom sow at this time, even in a heated greenhouse.

I say this in the hope that at some point over Christmas you will find the time and inclination to make like a plant (or a sleepy bear); sit back, lie back, even join the youth and kick back to get some commerce- and goal-free hibernation time of your own.

Having worked as a sales assistant in Harrods at Christmas many years ago (the worst sales assistant ever to be afflicted on their suede and leather department), I witnessed the waves of heaving, bargain-hunting, traumatised sales-season shoppers. An abiding aversion to the abomination of the ever-more-premature January sale has stayed with me. Give your credit card a rest. The nation will survive a week without it. Apart from keeping an eye on our cauliflowers, we finish work on the 24th – so no more boxes until January.

Enough subversive, left-leaning, anarchistic pontification for 2009. May your turkey be tender, your nut rissole delicious and your sprouts cooked to perfection. May you find contentment, happiness and convivial company to share it with. In short, Merry Christmas from us all at Riverford.

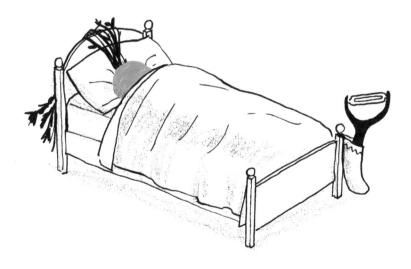

prophesies of doom

With growth all but stopped for the month there is not much to pick and it is too early for planting. In previous years we would be busy cutting cauliflowers for our co-op members who have fields running down to the coast, where the mild air from the sea gives a measure of protection from frost. But over the years they have begun to manage their own crops, which leaves us with some breathing space to catch up on all the jobs that normally get shunted to the bottom of the list in our busy ten-month season. January is now for mending rabbit fences, planting trees and scrapping the piles of machinery that have piled up over the years of indulgences at farm sales.

For me, January is also a month of reading. Every year my father's Christmas present is another weighty tome describing the impending downfall of our planet – normally as a result of multinational corporations and humankind's folly. This year it was 'The Long Emergency' by James Kunstler; a well-written description of the consequences of our collective unwillingness to face the reality that oil production has, or is about to, peak. This year, for the first time, I almost made it to the end, before it all became just too depressing and I cast it aside (to my wife's relief). There is only so much doom that can be taken in January. There seems little doubt that the developed world must act quickly and decisively to reduce the environmental, social and political impact of oil depletion and climate change, but no amount of rational and well-informed argument seems to be effective in changing our behaviour. The challenge is to make environmentalism attractive. Prophesies of doom, however well-founded, just turn people off.

To make matters worse, Professor James Lovelock, proposer of the 'Gaia hypothesis*', announced last week that we are already stuffed; climate change may have gone beyond the point of no return. If you are of a more optimistic disposition, you might like to know that organic farming only consumes about 60 per cent of the energy it takes to produce the same amount of conventionally-grown* food. Nitrogen fertiliser is the main cause for the difference – it consumes the equivalent of eight tonnes of oil to produce a ton of ammonium nitrate. In an organic system, clover does the same job using only energy from the sun. How the food is produced is only the start of the story; with 25 per cent of road freight being accounted for by food, the method of processing and distribution are just as important. We are starting a project with Exeter University to assess our environmental footprint (and socio-economic contribution) all the way from sowing a seed to delivering to your doorstep. We will keep you informed as the project progresses, provided the apocalypse holds off that long.

seeds of trouble?

Do you remember the full-page newspaper ads used by the agribusiness Monsanto* in 1998 when they were desperately trying to squash resistance to genetically-modified* crops in Europe? Their strapline was 'seeds of hope'. If you tune in to Radio 4 on Tuesday evening you will hear an excellent account of how GM crops have turned out to be seeds of trouble (the name of the programme) for just about everyone concerned.

Back in 1998, with the assistance of the Soil Association* and Friends of the Earth, I took the government to court to challenge the legality of a local trial of a variety of genetically-modified maize. For a while the farm was swarming with TV crews and journalists and we were regularly mentioned. We were even quoted on the Archers*.

I rapidly realised that I was not a born campaigner. To be effective in twenty-second sound bites, you need dogged persistence and a willingness to see issues in black and white. I believe that GM technology could, one day, be harnessed to benefit mankind in such a way that the risks were outweighed by the benefits to the environment. For this reason I feel uncomfortable condemning the technology in absolute and final terms. John Watson, my father, has none of my lily-livered ambivalence and has been campaigning and lobbying local and national government for the last five years. This week, Devon County Council will vote on whether Devon should become a GM-free zone. If it is successful, Somerset and Cornwall are expected to follow suit. I am amazed and delighted to find that this would have the backing of EU law.

The current range of GM crops being pushed by the biotech*
companies have been engineered to tolerate late applications
of the broad-spectrum herbicide, gluphinosate. Since there
have been no proper feeding trials or studies on the effect of
the herbicide, the risks are considerable and the benefits are
insignificant. I say "let the south-west be GM free", at least
until some crops are offered that might benefit more than
just biotech shareholders. Well done to all those dogged
letter-writers who have taken the issue this far.

the courgette 'crisis'

Last week I was interviewed on BBC Radio 4's Today programme about the great courgette 'crisis'. The word 'crisis' is questionable, but courgettes are indeed hard to come by; snow in Spain and extreme cold in Italy has killed many crops and brought others to a halt. Predictably, I advocated eating seasonal veg grown closer to home instead, but recent hard frosts have left greens of all sorts in short supply, even in Devon.

I suspect the term 'crisis' refers to the followers of 'clean eating', and in particular those fond of spiralising courgettes. I am inherently resistant to claims of 'superfoods', along with most dietary dogma. As I question whether the healthiness, or otherwise, of a food can be defined by one parameter, whether salt, saturated fat, carbs, alkalinity or even 'organicness'; I hope I have never made outlandish claims for my cabbages or cardoons. With forty years of scientific advice to switch from unprocessed 'natural' animal fats like butter to factory-made unsaturated fats like margarine now looking questionable, scepticism of conventional scientific advice is understandable. Unfortunately the highly-processed foods we should mainly avoid have the biggest budgets for advertising, lobbying and sponsoring the research which shapes our choices.

Who should we trust? Instinct might once have been a guide (as it is for animals) but probably not when standing in a supermarket aisle, where it is corrupted beyond usefulness by advertising, packaging, the food choices presented – plus a media more prone to extremes than balance. Our government's

'Eat Well Guide' is a good start, though even here I suspect commercial influence in places. Beware of anyone with a product or brand to sell and anyone quoting gurus, absolutes and pseudo-science. Instead I reckon writer Michael Pollan's (I paraphrase) "Eat less, mostly plants, and only things your grandmother would recognise as food" is a reasonable place to start.

the question of meat

My father gave me a pig for my eighth birthday. He didn't believe in pocket money; the idea was that the pig would be the first of many and an introduction to farming and business. My pig faithfully produced thirteen healthy piglets twice a year, but I didn't share my father's passion for pig-keeping (for forty years, as so many farmers moved towards factory farming, his enthusiasm was trying to develop an ethically-acceptable way of keeping them). I moved onto sheep, then milking cows before finding my vocation with vegetables.

That cabbage epiphany came nearly twenty-five years ago and, to this day, my enthusiasm remains for vegetables – though I'm not a vegetarian. Meanwhile, my brother Ben used those pigs to teach himself charcuterie and set up a farm shop in our garage, which thirty years later has developed into three shops and the meat boxes that we offer alongside the vegetables. Our siblings Oliver and Louise developed the cows and the dairy business and now raise some of the bull calves for our beef. Our soils at Wash Farm in Devon are not inherently very fertile and we would really struggle to grow veg without the manure from these cows. On top of that, at least a third of the farm is too steep, or the soil too thin, to be suitable for anything other than grazing livestock.

We have many vegetarian customers and get the occasional letter questioning our position on meat, so the point of these ramblings is to give an agricultural and historical perspective. As a nation we undoubtedly eat more meat than is good for our health or the environment. Indeed, if we are to have any chance of feeding the world's burgeoning population whilst retaining any balance and beauty on our planet we must radically reduce our collective appetite for meat, dairy and poultry. So our position is to encourage the meat-eaters among us to eat less and better. This means feeding sheep and cows their natural diet (grass and clover, not grain), hanging meat properly and always using the whole carcass to best effect. Think thrifty pies, hashes and making stock with every last scrap. If we are going to eat meat, we should be smarter about it.

more ruminating on protein

"Dad, how can you call yourself an environmentalist, and still sell meat?" First one daughter, then the other, then even my previously carnivorous sons joined in. Their epiphany was brought on by the documentary 'Cowspiracy'. It is smug, irritating and outrageously one-sided in its selection of evidence, and ends with an unjustified and ill-considered swipe at Greenpeace. However, despite my irritation with it, I would agree (uncomfortably for someone selling meat) that no-one can reasonably claim to be an environmentalist, or even a humanist, while continuing to eat more than very small amounts of animal protein. Animal agriculture is simply wrecking our planet.

Climate-change-wise the arguments are complex, involving ruminant methane emissions, deforestation for grazing and soya production, methane- and nitrous-oxide-emitting manure heaps and soil, intensive versus extensive farming methods and more. As our planet is so diverse in soils, topography, ecology, diet and agricultural methods, it's unwise to be dogmatic. However, after weeks scouring scientific papers, we have reached the following initial conclusions:

~ Livestock agriculture contributes 10-12 per cent of man-made climate change; arguably as much as every car, plane, truck and ship on the planet.

~ Livestock agriculture is grossly inefficient and requires five to ten times more land to feed ourselves than a vegan diet; there just isn't enough land to go round.

OK, it's not that simple; there may well be a credible argument for animals grazing permanent pastures on land unsuited for growing crops for humans, to produce high-quality, high-welfare meat and dairy, but we will have to consume much less of it. Alongside this are all the health, animal-welfare, pollution and antibiotic-resistance arguments against eating meat; hard to quantify, but very real. There will be exceptions, but the general conclusion is inescapable: for the good of our own health and that of our planet, we must collectively eat much less animal protein.

20TH FEBRUARY 2006

fordhall farm

When I started growing organic vegetables twenty years ago,
I spent a good deal of time travelling the country picking the
brains of farmers and growers in a bid to minimise the number
of mistakes I would make in my new venture. Everyone was
incredibly helpful and almost invariably I was offered a bed
for the night, be it in a mansion or a caravan. There was a good
smattering of eccentricity and a bit of genius amongst those
far-sighted freaks on the fringes. Many of them were a generation
(or two or three) ahead of their time. Most cared little for public
approval and, in the absence of today's interest, many struggled
to make ends meet financially. They were driven by a passion
for discovering the secrets of managing a healthy soil.

A few years later, when I was starting to find my feet, I was
commissioned by the Gaia Foundation (an environmental
organisation) to visit Fordhall Farm in Shropshire and write a
report on the viability of a radically different system of cultivation
being developed there by the legendary farmer Arthur Hollins.
Arthur was grappling with the contradiction that strikes all good
organic farmers when they need to create a seed bed; namely that
as custodians of the soil, we are painfully aware that anything we
do to disturb its natural balance is to the detriment of the tens of
thousands of species that make their home there. Most of us settle
for ploughing (as shallowly as possible) as a necessary evil, but
Arthur had developed a revolutionary machine that skimmed
off the top inch or two of turf, pulverised it and scattered it gently
on top of the sowed seed in one operation. He was one of the

most enquiring and inspiring people I have met and in two days with him, my understanding of the soil, and in particular the importance of keeping it covered in the winter, advanced hugely.

Arthur recently died after eighty years of developing his pioneering farming system at Fordhall. The farm still does a huge amount of work with schools and the public, but it is threatened by development. The owners have given Arthur's family until July to find the £800,000 to buy the farm or it will be sold from under them. They would like to keep it going as an educational, community-owned resource and, from what I have seen, have the skills and determination to make it work. We are going to support them: if all farmers had a little bit of Arthur's empathy with their soil, England would be a greener and more pleasant land.

7,500 people raised £600,000, with the another £100,000 coming from interest-free loans to buy the farm. It is now in community ownership and run by Arthur's children, Ben and Charlotte.

gm revisited & golden rice

Fifteen years ago I took the government to the High Court in London to challenge the legality of some genetically-modified* maize trials bordering our farm in Devon. Encouraged by my father and a group of radicals from the nearby town of Totnes, I read a stack of scientific papers and felt sufficiently concerned to accept support from Friends of the Earth and the Soil Association* and hire a lawyer. We lost in court but won in the papers, which turned out to be more important. Our opponents, the multinational agribusiness Monsanto*, struck back with intensive lobbying and adverts featuring images of starving children. They claimed their technology would feed the world (despite little evidence of increased yields and much evidence of GM being unaffordable for small-scale farmers).

Did this justify the selective and emotive use of evidence on our side? A friend recently sent photos of a group of us posing for the press outside the High Court, holding banners and some wearing Frankenstein masks. I regret the masks; we were debasing what should have been a sober debate. To this day, it remains very hard to access quality information that is not tainted by dogma, promise of commercial gain or naive fascination with technology.

No one will convince me that GM crops are completely safe for us or the environment, but that is not sufficient for me to completely condemn them. The debate should be about whether the benefits outweigh the risks. My reading suggests that, to date, the only significant beneficiaries have been shareholders from a few global corporations, with some marginal, short-term gains to large-scale monoculture farmers growing for the world market. Health risks seems to be smaller than I thought fifteen years ago, but alongside GM there appears to have been an overall increase in pesticide use, and there is still no consistent evidence of yield benefits. The risk/benefits equation does not add up. With two million people dying a year from vitamin-A deficiency (GM-advocates' figure), could genetically-modified 'golden', vitamin-enhanced rice change the equation? I wish I could fight my way through the spin to information I trust; but then I helped to start it.

our once omnivorous swine

When I was a schoolboy, my father's annual act of civic responsibility was to run the 'bowling for the pig' stand at the village fête. The winner got a real, live weaner (piglet) to take home and fatten up. Food rationing having ended just ten years earlier, shortages were still fresh in many memories in a rural area. The idea of fattening a pig in your garden using kitchen waste wasn't so weird.

Pigs have been valued around the globe for centuries for their ability to eat just about anything, and thereby turn waste into food. Our pigs were fed whey* mixed with home-grown barley, ground in our own mill. Waste from our unappetising school lunches was collected by the swill man and cooked down to feed to pigs, as was the case across the country. As rationing ended in 1954, chickens and pigs were the first to succumb to the progression to factory farming. Unwilling to go down this route, we sold our last pigs in the '90s as my father, a lifelong pig enthusiast, retired.

Fifty years on, despite the BBC's Good Life and the revival of 'make do and mend', if I offered a weaner at a fête today I'd probably be arrested or committed. Both conventional* and organic pigs are fed on barley or wheat mixed with soya; animals that once ate waste are competing for food with the world's poor and contributing to deforestation and loss of wildlife as more and more land is used to grow soya. Using food waste to feed pigs has been banned since the foot-and-mouth outbreak of 2001, as untreated swill is widely considered to be the source of the epidemic. Yet with careful management, a return to recycling food waste in this way (as championed by campaigners The Pig Idea*) would reduce our reliance on imported soya and so lessen the environmental devastation that comes with it. Meanwhile I'm seriously considering introducing a small herd of hardy pigs into our woods, fattening them up on our veg waste. Pa spent fifty years losing money by keeping pigs, but it never crushed his enthusiasm. I must have inherited something from him.

every-meat bolognese

Personally, I don't have a problem with eating horse. It might make perfect sense to eat a fallen racehorse or a Dartmoor pony at the end of its life. Even Romanian carthorse might be OK in a stew. But I would rather make that choice myself, with some idea of how the horse got to my table, including credible assurance of how the animal lived and died. I don't want untraceable 'everyday value' red goo turning up on my plate because supermarkets put too much pressure on their suppliers.

There may be no risk to our health from this meat (as one public health official pointed out, not so reassuringly, the salt and fat in these processed foods will get you first anyway). The horse may well have had a better life than your average, quick-grown, grain-stuffed beef animal that has never left the yard or tasted grass; but horsegate* makes a mockery of supermarket reassurances about sourcing and traceability. If you relentlessly buy on price, someone will find a cheaper way of doing things, however many bits of paper you make them fill in.

Have no doubt, there is a cost to producing food to the standards most of us want. There is an even greater cost to taking the trouble of doing it yourself or only buying in from people you completely trust. We live in a world of brands where practically everything is outsourced to the lowest bidder on the world market. Sometimes there is a good reason why something can be done more cheaply by someone unknown on the other side of the world. Sometimes it is because they are doing things that are convenient for you not to know about.

Ninety-five percent of the veg, meat, fruit, eggs, dairy, bread, preserves and pies we sell comes either from our farm, a member of my family, our co-op or other farmers we know well and have worked with for years. Spending time together (preferably in the field, but a pub also works) is the best way of ensuring quality and integrity in the food chain.

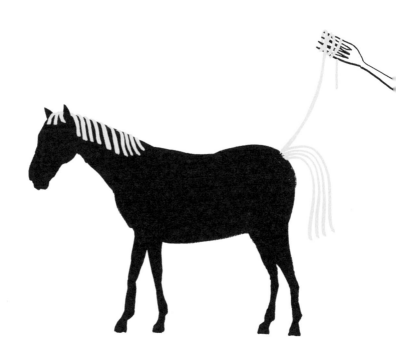

more than you needed to know about muck

The winters of my childhood were dominated by muck. Two hundred cows produce a lot of it and the dung pit always seemed to be spilling out into the yard, making shifting it a constant challenge. It might not sound idyllic, but I enjoyed it, apart from the pig muck (that was just too stinky).

If you have ventured into the countryside recently, you might have noticed the smell (the muck is flying, the slurry gushing). With the soil dryer than it has been for eleven months, it's the ideal time for spreading manure. Some farmers fling it, some dribble it, some inject it straight into the soil. The main problem is that the stuff is produced from housed cattle in the winter, when the ground is normally too wet to spread it, and the dormant soil and crops cannot absorb it. My innovative father would send it gushing down a trench, which followed the contour around the hill, to where his welly-clad children would create dams and breaches to allow it to trickle down the slope to feed the pasture. Later, with the arrival of better pumps, came the exploding bladder, which slowly inflated with slurry, until every few minutes, unannounced, it would purge itself across the field. The smell was horrendous. The latest development in muck technology is the umbilical pipe: slurry is pumped from the cow yards down up to a mile of snaking pipe to a tractor fitted with low-ground-pressure tyres and a dribble bar. This zig-zags around the farm, spreading the muck evenly without the damage caused to the soil by huge tankers and spreaders – a massive improvement.

Cheap synthetic fertiliser can lead conventional* farmers to view muck as something to get rid of as cheaply as possible. Once upon a time, too much of it ended up polluting rivers – although farmers have cleaned up their act and this is now very rare. Organic farmers have always prized their muck. Recycling nutrients back into the soil, matching availability to crop root absorption with a minimum of loss to leaching or the atmosphere is vital to our success. It's a bit stinky sometimes, but we'd be lost without it.

draying the voyers

The margins of the field, where the horses would once have been turned around during ploughing, have as many different names as there are countries. Our local name for these awkward pieces of the field, which must be cultivated after the rest is finished, is the 'voyers'. All respectable ploughmen would try to plough a field so that the furrow was turned up the hill, to counteract the tendency of the soil to move down the slope, but even this was not enough. Over the years it would result in the soil becoming thin or 'bony' on the top voyer, as it moved down the field to accumulate on the 'fatter' bottom voyer. To compensate for this it was stipulated in some tenancy agreements that, every few years, the tenant would 'dray the voyers', which meant hauling a set number of cartloads from the bottom to the top.

It is a point of contention between my dairy-farming brother and me that my vegetables, and all the cultivations required to make a fine seedbed, result in an excessive movement of soil down the field. This is particularly the case on the steeper south-facing fields that we value so highly for our early crops. As a condition of our continuing to share these warm fields, he has insisted we re-instigate the time-honoured practice. Next week, provided the dry weather continues, before planting the first cabbages, we will first be draying our voyers. We will use a bulldozer and a team of 120-horsepower tractors, rather than one-horsepower carts and a shovel, but I hope my neighbours will be impressed.

With high pressure anchored over the North Atlantic, the wind has been in the north for almost a month bringing some very welcome cold, dry and bright weather. This has enabled us to spread all the manure that the cows have been busy making since they came in from the pastures in October. It is wonderful to be able to do this at the perfect time while the ground is so unseasonably dry. All the fields destined for early crops have been ploughed and we have planted the first potatoes, carrots and onions in ideal conditions. We would have expected to be very busy with the time-consuming job of harvesting purple sprouting broccoli, but, as with most crops, growth is almost completely arrested below seven degrees Celsius, so psb is conspicuously absent from most of the boxes. With the rapidly lengthening days, there will be deluge as soon as it gets a bit warmer.

MARCH TO MAY
hungry gap

The last of the kale, cauliflowers and
leeks are running to seed. Even with cold
storage, the potatoes, onions and carrots
are sprouting. Weather permitting, planting
starts in earnest in March. But even the
sprinting pak choi, radishes and first lettuce
will not be ready before mid-May. The diehard
localists get hungry and frustrated. The more
pragmatic look to Spain and Italy to maintain
some variety in the kitchen. We all wait
impatiently for another year to begin.

lusty leeks &
previous potatoes

My cockerel is getting vocal and the hens are going broody.
The calendar tells us that spring is here. It may not feel like it
outside, but the biological clock is ticking inside our vegetables,
telling them to wake up and reproduce, expecting warmth and
sunshine. For roots, tubers and bulbs, nature's carbohydrate
stores, this means breaking dormancy and sending out shoots.
These shoots are controlled in the conventional* industry by
the use of chemical sprout suppressants. Our only tool is to keep
potatoes etc. cold in an attempt to fool them that we are still in
the depths of winter. They will wake up fast as soon as they come
out of our stores and in to your kitchens; try to keep them cool
and don't expect them to last for more than three weeks.

Leeks are also upping their efforts to reproduce. If you slice
them in half lengthways you will see the apical meristem in the
centre where the new leaves are initiated by cell division. About
this time their clock tells the meristem to stop producing leaves
and to initiate an embryonic flower. This is carried upwards,
accelerating as the days get longer, to emerge as a 'bolt' in
mid-April. They would flower in May if they got the chance.
I hope you will have eaten them all before then. We try to
leave the precociously-flowering individuals in the field. If you
encounter one in your kitchen you will find that they still eat
well until the bolt turns woody when it should be discarded.

digging up granny

From September we will have to feed the contents of the meals we cook for our local school into a computer which will tot up the nutrients and tell our cook if they are fit to eat. I am sure this initiative is full of good intentions, and it may even help to reduce some abuses at the lower end of school catering, but it strikes me as depressingly reductionist, culturally degrading and an intrinsically unhealthy approach to food.

In a recent edition of Radio Four's excellent Food Programme, Michael Pollan, author of 'In Defence of Food', gave some simple guidance on how to eat a healthy diet and enjoy it:

1. don't eat anything your great-grandmother would not recognise as food
2. don't buy anything with more than five ingredients
3. only eat at a table; eat slowly and communally
4. distrust any food claiming health benefits

This all made so much sense that I bought the book, the gist being that your granny is a better source of dietary guidance than science and nutrition experts. Having spent five years studying natural sciences I am wary of unquestioning adulation of native wisdom, but when it comes to nutrition, science has earned a bad name. Our relationship with food is far more complex than simply summing up the known nutrients and multiplying by their known effects on our bodies – there is just too much that we do not know. Judging from a recent article in 'New Scientist', we are still far from understanding the relationship of appetite, diet and weight gain – but this has not prevented the proliferation of highly-processed functional foods marketed on their ability to fight coronary heart disease and help weight loss.

Science will not solve a cultural problem; namely a collapse in the willingness, confidence and skills needed to cook and enjoy real food. There is no one healthy diet, no silver bullet that can better the knowledge, accumulated over generations, of how to use predominantly locally-sourced ingredients to sustain us through happy and healthy lives. Pollan's advice is that unless you suffer from a specific illness like diabetes, the best thing to do with a nutritionist's advice is to ignore it.

tony gets his way again

The variety of genetically-modified* maize 'Chardon LL' was given approval to be grown in the UK last week. This is the variety that was trialled adjacent to our farm in 1998, resulting in my legal challenge to the government. The case went all the way to the High Court and helped to raise public and media awareness of the issue (though we lost). After six years of debate it all hinged on a piece of fairly spurious research comparing a GM crop sprayed with glufosinate (a herbicide which kills everything) with a non-GM crop which had been sprayed with atrazine (kills almost everything for longer). As atrazine is one of the most persistent and environmentally-devastating chemicals used in agriculture (and has now been banned anyway) it is hardly very reassuring to know that in the short term, at least, it was less damaging. Essentially, all this trial showed was that one herbicide (atrazine) was more environmentally-damaging than another (glufosinate). The experiment did not address the question of whether the crop itself was safe. Like so many of Tony Blair's decisions, the facts had been patiently and painstakingly distorted to suit his personal ideology. There is nothing more dangerous than a man who believes he is right.

The British Medical Association even came out in favour of glufosinate in the end, saying that it was a question of balancing risks and benefits and that the risks were very small. I could almost agree because I think the risks of any devastating damage to health or environment probably are fairly small. But where are the benefits they were balancing those risks with? The yield or quality is no higher and I am sure that food will be no better or cheaper as a result. The only benefit is that, for a period of perhaps three years, the farmer will find it marginally easier to control weeds in the crop by applying glufosinate. This chemical will kill all plants apart from the GM crop that has had a bacterium T25 gene inserted, giving it resistance. I cannot think why any farmer would want to grow it given this tiny benefit, which no doubt will be all but compensated for by the higher cost of the seed. Experience in the USA suggests that after three years weeds will be starting to acquire resistance to the glufosinate anyway.

If this was a crop that had increased drought resistance or was able to grow with less fertiliser or pesticide, there might be some argument. To allow a farmer to be even more devastatingly effective in removing the last vestiges of wildlife from his field does not seem an adequate benefit to warrant any risk at all. Let's hope that British farmers are smart enough not to grow the stuff.

11TH APRIL 2011
ploughing, perennials
& dozing farmers

Farmers love ploughing. Through March and April, every time the weather's right, we are out there methodically turning the green fields brown; burying the weeds and last year's crop debris and creating clean seedbeds. Turning around on the tractor seat to see four unbroken furrows sequentially skimmed, cut, and lifted to lie perfectly inverted with their neighbours, stretching back down the field, is one of the most satisfying tasks imaginable. John Scott, who taught me the skill, claimed to have ploughed every field in the parish with a horse; a dubious assertion, but he was certainly a master at his craft.

However, much as I enjoy ploughing, it is a recklessly hedonistic pleasure which plagues me with guilt. Organic farming is based on the principle of working in harmony with nature; aiming to grow food with the least disruption to the systems that have supported our planet for millennia. To rely on such a violent (imagine being an earthworm or fragile fungal mycorrhiza*) annual event to establish our crops is clearly a contradiction. Life is full of compromises and we try to reduce the damage by ploughing shallowly and giving the fields long breaks under grass clover leys, but I would dearly love to find a better way.

The most inspiring agriculture I have witnessed was a small farm in Uganda where crops were grown in an apparently chaotic (but actually skilfully-managed) mixture. With several canopies and a predominance of perennial crops, the farm had much in common with the virgin forest nearby. The result was hugely productive (about twenty times more than the monoculture next door) and the farmer seemed to spend most of the time relaxing under a tree. Might such a system be possible here? Conditions are very different – climate, expensive labour and reliance on machinery etc. – but I am confident that that Ugandan farmer had more to teach me than I ever had to teach him about how to feed nine million people without destroying the planet.

the springs have sprung

The farm is awash with springs breaking out where I have never seen them before. With sodden fields and no sign of break in the weather we are starting to get nervous about our early plantings of lettuce, cabbage, potatoes and carrots as well as the rhubarb; they should all be in the ground by now. The soil is warm and the first plants are ready to leave the protection of the greenhouse and start life in the field, but it will take several days of dry weather before our soil becomes friable, allowing us to make a seedbed without causing damage to the soil's structure.

Meanwhile, the overwintered crops planted last summer are thriving in the lengthening days and warm temperatures. The purple sprouting broccoli is finally heading up and will be in most boxes most weeks for the next two months and there are plenty of cauliflowers to cut. We have the added bonus of being able to pick re-growth from our chard and curly kale. This means that even as we go into the 'hungry gap', we have been able to keep the boxes 70 per cent UK-grown (higher if you exclude the fruit). We could get even higher still if we could persuade our growers to grow more onions; it really annoys me having to buy them from Holland. We have sold a few surplus cauliflowers to other box schemes recently, but generally, unless you really start screaming at us, it is our intention to continue with the local, in-season theme until our fields are empty in early May. There is then the inevitable gap before the new season crops arrive (assuming it has stopped raining and we have planted them), when we will have to resort to some imports.

fleeces & leather jackets

The recent dry weather has allowed us to make some perfect
seedbeds, but the cold, easterly winds have been testing for the
young lettuce, calabrese* and cabbage plants which we have
been planting straight from the greenhouses.

At this time of year we would normally cover them with a
fleece* cover to keep the cold, drying winds off, but this year
we are plagued by voracious hordes of leather jackets. These are
the fat, grey-brown, large-mouthed larvae of daddy-long-legs.
The adults lay their eggs in grass or clover leys in the late summer.
As part of our rotation, we plough these leys in early spring.
The eggs hatch and are just building up their appetite as
we plant out the tender young plants.

Our only allies are flocks of crows and heavy ground-rolling.
The crows go crazy for the fat grubs and can clean up a field
in a few weeks. Rolling firms the ground and makes it hard for
the grubs to move around and find the plants. It is satisfying
(but probably a fantasy) to think that the rolling might squash
a few grubs as well. After having the first covered planting of
cabbage wiped out, we inspected all the freshly-ploughed fields
and found them to be heaving with pestilent, greedy grubs.
We have decided to leave the fleeces off to allow the crows in
to do their work. Despite some very cold-looking plants this
policy seems to be working.

trendy, treacherous ransoms

A few years ago, inspired by a wild-garlic omelette, we started foraging for wild garlic (known locally as ransoms) in the woods on our farm in Devon. What started as a source of pocket money for my children soon became so popular in the veg boxes that we had a team spending much of the spring on their knees, gathering these deliciously pungent leaves.

Then disaster struck. For a brief period in March and April before the trees come into full leaf, ransoms form a dense ground cover. Unfortunately, the same growing conditions that favour wild garlic also favour a plant called lords-and-ladies, which has a leaf similar in colour and texture to wild garlic, but is toxic. It happened; an errant leaf made it through and we concluded that we couldn't take the risk.

Three years later wild garlic is on the menu of every trendy eatery and has even made it to the shelves of more adventurous shops at thirty pounds per kilo or more. It seemed that maybe we had been uncharacteristically risk-averse. To explore the issue I had a small test nibble on lords-and-ladies myself. It felt like a fox had sprayed in my mouth and washed it down with sulphuric acid. A search of the web suggests the sensation in the mouth (caused by needle-like oxalate crystals) is so rapidly unpleasant that it would be hard to eat enough to cause lasting harm.

Bolstered by my guinea-pig trials, we have decided to try again and be very, very careful with our picking and to check again in the barn as we bag.

My enthusiasm for wild garlic is not limited to omelettes and salads; it is also one of the most sustainable foods we could eat and is in season at the heart of the hungry gap when local greens are in short supply. In the longer run I have plans to gather seeds and introduce it to the many acres of new deciduous woods that have been planted on the farm. Meanwhile, all being well, wild garlic will be on the extras list for the next two or three weeks.

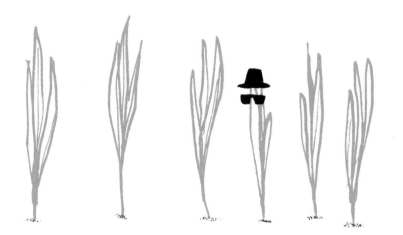

for love of the soil

If the weather forecasters are right, by the time you get this, there will be a big, high-pressure system anchored to the north, bringing cold, dry, easterly winds and we will be busy planting rhubarb, onions, lettuce, cabbage, potatoes and carrots. After a winter of planning, servicing machinery and tree-planting everyone is impatient to get the new season started.

The BBC Radio 4 Food Programme last week focused on the causes of an alarming 25 to 75 per cent decline in the vitamin and mineral content of our fruit and veg since 1940. Typically, the industry trade bodies are doing their best to muddy the waters, but the evidence is pretty clear and, by implication, damning of modern agricultural and food-retailing practice. The decline could be attributable to any one – or more likely a combination – of: changes in variety, packaging and storage techniques; the degradation of our soils resulting from increased use of synthetic fertilisers and pesticides; the neglect of rotations and animal manures.

People who get seriously animated about soil tend to be fairly eccentric. In twenty-seven years of studying agriculture I have yet to meet a soil scientist who could relate normally to the rest of the population. Perhaps it is their frustration with everyone else's ignorance and lack of interest in their subject. Our planet and our nutrition are so dependent on the microbial life of the soil; people should be more interested.

Lady Eve Balfour, the founder of the Soil Association*, by most accounts lacked social skills, but there can be no doubting

her determination and far-sighted wisdom when it came
to farming. In the 1940s, at a time when most women of her
class would have been eating cucumber sandwiches, she was
researching and writing her book 'The Living Soil' in which
she argued that the health of the soil, livestock and humans
was intrinsically and fundamentally linked.

A well-farmed organic soil, when compared to intensively-
farmed arable soils, will have many times the numbers of
beneficial bacteria, fungi and invertebrates which help to recycle
organic matter and protect crops from disease. In particular,
mycorrhizal* fungi, which live in symbiotic association with
plant roots, massively increase the root's surface area and help
the crop to access nutrients which could otherwise be unavailable.
Soil ecology is largely invisible to the uninitiated and its complexity
mainly defeats modern science, but if you have the time, tap
'Lady Eve Balfour' or 'mycorrhiza' into Google. Fascinating
stuff (but watch out for your social skills).

so much for the drought...

Here in Devon the reservoirs are full, the river is topping its banks, our fields are sodden and planting has ground to halt. The crops that are already in the ground are lapping up the water, especially the leafy brassicas, but this should be our busiest time for planting. With a current backlog of 250,000 plants, we'll have a gap when it comes to picking in May and June.

The gardeners among you will appreciate that, at these times, there's a world of difference between a light, sandy soil ('boy's land'), an intermediate loam*, and a heavy clay ('man's land'). Sandy soils are made up of relatively big, widely-spaced particles which allow rain to drain quickly through, and you need far less horsepower to make a fine seedbed. The downside is that they dry out quickly in summer and do not hold on to soluble nutrients. Conventional* veg growers with access to irrigation and synthetic fertiliser love them for their predictability and ease of cultivation. Clay soils have smaller particles, which absorb a lot of water and nutrients and give them up slowly to plant roots, making them less prone to drought and potentially very productive if managed well. The problem is that they require lots of power and skill to cultivate effectively; they are unstable when wet (that's why they smear and stick to your boots) and bake out like bricks when dry. As such, they need to be worked at just the right stage of drying. Loams are somewhere in between, being a mixture of sand, clay and organic matter. They are often the best soils, especially for organic farming where we like some clay to aid fertility.

Over centuries the soil beneath our feet has shaped the agriculture, landscape and wildlife above, so its influence is greater than you might first think. Where you see livestock, lots of grass, small fields and oaks growing, you can be pretty sure there's clay. Knowing and managing each field according to its type is critical to farming success; right now it would be handy to have a few acres of sand to get out on, but we have an intermediate soil and must wait. On the whole our land is pretty good though, if a little thin and steep. Besides, I have a (largely unproven) prejudice that balanced intermediate soils grow the tastiest veg, so I'm not complaining.

random rants

I've had a few perennial obsessions that can't be plausibly attached to a season. They sit here, a good number repeated from our first book, the Riverford Farm Cookbook.

beware the freaks
from the fringe

I remember being taught that evolutionary progress happens
on the fringes: whilst the dominant, overtly successful species
(currently us) are busy thriving, specialising, multiplying and
basically doing more of the same, the less successful, freakish
creatures are banished to the harsher fringes, where they scratch
a precarious existence and await their day. For most freaks it
never comes, and they perish without a fossil or obituary to
mark their struggle.

Our planet is constantly changing, however, and no one stays
at the centre forever. The fine adaptation and specialisation that
bring a species success ultimately prove its downfall. Dinosaurs
dominated earth for 160 million years until, 65 million years
ago, a 10-kilometre wide asteroid crashed into Mexico and upset
the conditions in which they thrived. They couldn't adapt to the
new reality and were gone in an evolutionary blink.

In so many ways, business follows the same patterns as nature:
survival of the fittest is one with obvious appeal for many post-
Thatcherite worshippers of the free market and globalisation.
Response to change is something on which those at the centre,
growing fat on the status quo, tend to be less keen.

Organic farmers were freaks from the fringe until very
recently. They typically lived in isolation in the depths of
Wales or Devon, where no self-respecting, tweed-clad, country
landowning Barley Baron would soil their fat, oversized Range
Rover tyres. Some were even women and one or two wore

sandals, woolly jumpers and beards and had the occasional dope plant hidden amongst the tomatoes. They were derided for decades. Surely it would take a massive intergalactic collision for this lot to threaten or displace mainstream farming and food retailing, which is fiercely protected by a well-heeled agribusiness and backed up by a powerful global agrichemical sector?

Change has been driven more by an asteroid shower than a single meteor: BSE, foot-and-mouth, pesticide and fertiliser pollution and contamination, global warming, 'peak oil', public concern over the excesses of food transportation, routine antibiotic misuse, the imposition of genetic manipulation, revulsion at factory farming and the normalisation of the abuses of a food industry where a chicken can quite legally be only 50 per cent chicken, the rest made up of beef gristle and water. The soft underbelly of success is complacency, and the accompanying lack of imagination and willingness to learn. Within the mainstream, there is little genuine desire to adapt to a new climate of well-founded public concern. A few ground-breaking organic brands have been bought by Cadbury, Dean Foods, Unilever and the like, and a fair amount has been spent on greenwash-inspired PR initiatives and Corporate Responsibility Indexes, but behind the smokescreen little has changed. Could we be witnessing the start of a mass extinction of global agri-food businesses? For decades, they have seemed immovable and omnipotent in their power – but then so did the dinosaurs, until the last one found itself being chased around by a bone-wielding, two-legged freak previously seen rubbing two sticks together in a cave.

keeping the faith

Farmers are a stubbornly independent lot who tend to spend too much time in their own company. Most organic farmers are no different, so it is a bit misleading when people talk about the organic 'movement' – a word that carries connotations of a unanimous tide of opinion, or even gurus and mindless followers. Few things could be further from the truth. Organic farming boasts a host of freethinking individuals, each with their own pet enthusiasm, often verging on obsession, that has been developed in isolation on their farms and only occasionally tempered by an audience more challenging than a flock of sheep. They can be a bit extreme, and grouping them together is like trying to herd a yardful of cats. Organic is a broad church that constantly re-evaluates itself and has its share of schisms along the way.

I feel uncomfortable about some aspects of the organic certification standards and the broader movement: I feel no allegiance to those who use organic food as a form of snobbery or those who see it simply as the latest way of maximising their short-term farm income or developing a brand. Some organically certified practices, particularly in the areas of poultry and dairy, where production is concentrated in the hands of ever larger producers, make me uncomfortable. Given a free hand, I might use some seed treatments where a tiny quantity of chemical would massively ease the challenge of growing crops at a price that makes them accessible to everyone. I have done my share of cantankerous objecting to these things but I am still in the church and toeing the certified line.

At times I have wavered and considered simply doing it my own way according to the standards of my conscience and beliefs about food and farming – perhaps becoming the farming equivalent of Martin Bell* as an independent politician. That way we would end up with 101 different standards, and customers would have to have the patience to listen to a diatribe about the subtle differences of each. On top of deciding which brand of recycled loo roll to buy or whether to offset their carbon, few people have the time. So we must all put up with an approximation to our own preferred standard. For me, being certified by the Soil Association* is a shorthand way of describing more or less how I want to farm. It is close enough and allows me to be able to farm without boring everyone with the details of why I do it the way I do.

Over the years I have reached the conclusion that few people who buy organic food really understand the specifics of organic farming (why should they when the regulations extend to 400 pages?) but most do have an intuitive trust, amongst the insanities and abuses of modern food and farming, that organic farming is right for us and right for our planet. And for the most part it is. Perhaps even more importantly, by moving organic farming in the right direction we are dragging conventional* farming along with it.

has cooking become a spectator activity?

Two decades of celebrity chefs and TV cookery, endless pages of glossy food porn, combined with government five-a-day campaigns, have done little to avert the decline in activity in most kitchens. We may be conversant with the language of a multicultural twenty-first-century foodie but many of us are at a loss as to what to do with a Savoy cabbage or a piece of brisket. How can a nation so interested in food have seen the percentage of household income devoted to it slip from 33 to 15 per cent over fifty years? It continues to fall.

We have all the symptoms of a national eating disorder, with an astonishing ability to disconnect perception and professed beliefs about food from reality and behaviour. Despite the best efforts of Jamie, Hugh, Gordon, Nigella et al., less cooking than ever is going on. Moreover, the few unprocessed ingredients in our kitchens are even less seasonal than ten years ago. When we started the box scheme in 1993, before the current media frenzy around local and seasonal, our typical customer ordered a weekly box of seasonal vegetables and cooked them with little fuss, probably much as their parents had, with the addition of the occasional curry or stir-fry. Fifteen years later, when all the column inches would suggest that such behaviour was a national movement, the number of people willing and able to cook within seasonal limitations, has, if anything, declined. Our longstanding core customers carry on cooking, but some newer recruits show limited appetite for what we really like to grow and sell: seasonal, homegrown veg. They will buy the fruit and the tomatoes, the broccoli and the peppers but many reject even moderate amounts of the core seasonal roots and greens which demand more traditional cooking skills.

Why this mismatch of aspiration and behaviour? Memories of appalling school dinners don't help vegetables such as cabbages and swede, and a dogmatic adherence to 'local' can be hard work in April and May, but I am convinced that a lack of time, confidence and skills in the kitchen is the main issue. Indeed, I suspect that some of the media attention may have actually sapped confidence, and made cooking seem unattainably distant.

Food fashions, as portrayed in the media and on restaurant menus, come and go like the cut of a pair of jeans, yet all over the world food is a conservative force. For generations, we learned from our parents how to make the best use of local ingredients; changes in real-life home cooking were slow and incremental. The last forty years has broken this tradition, helped along by the advertising budgets of food manufacturers and supermarkets, beamed out from the same televisions that have ensured we 'don't have time to cook'. It has taken two generations to decline to the culinary trough that we now wallow in. We are now raising a generation whose parents will rarely be seen cooking and even more rarely with local ingredients. Cookery programmes are a poor substitute for assimilating skills over years growing up in an active kitchen. There is undeniably a counter-current emerging, but it is a small eddy in the general flow of decline. Though our celebrity chefs and food writers must take some credit for this change, the battle is far from won and there is a real danger that, as the gap widens between what is on television and the reality in our kitchens, cooking will become a spectator activity.

where did all the
growers go?

A trip around the formerly thriving traditional horticultural areas of the UK reveals a depressing picture of dilapidated glasshouses, machinery gently rusting under brambles and horticulture disappearing under wheat, as the skills and associated culture of a once-proud industry, built up over generations, are lost for ever. Be it the Vale of Evesham, the Isle of Thanet, the mosses of Lancashire, the Tamar Valley or the orchards of Kent, the story is one of an industry on its knees, drawing its last gasps before quietly slipping beneath the sod.

Until thirty years ago, these areas supplied the neighbouring conurbations with most of their seasonal fruit and vegetables, initially through thriving wholesale markets and then increasingly through supermarkets, which were at that time happy to buy locally. The last generation of growers has seen supermarkets become increasingly dominant and progressively impose trading terms that can be met only by the largest companies. The smaller regional growers have quietly gone to the wall, to be replaced by agribusinesses employing gang labour in vast factories, often under highly questionable working conditions. Continuity and consistency are achieved with the help of aircraft streaming into Heathrow and fleets of trucks from southern Europe, so that shoppers are never troubled by the seasons or the vagaries of the weather.

Change happens and, one might argue, why should horticulture be any different from the coal, steel or shipbuilding industries? The difference is that this change is unnecessary, wasteful and, in a world threatened by climate change and oil depletion, unsustainable. It is not the result of market forces but of oligopoly. Supermarket supply chains, with their technology, protocols and audits, are fantastically efficient at the centralised distribution of uniform, continuously available products from large suppliers who obediently follow their rules. They struggle badly with the human interactions typical of smaller-scale, local businesses. Many supermarket customers want local food and would like to feel some connection with where it is produced, but somehow the sterile aisles have swept us along with the ridiculous pretence that vegetables can be produced with the uniform, hygienic perfection to match the plastic trays and shelves they sit on. Supermarkets, with their overpackaged, anonymously own-brand, travel-weary offerings, are only now, reluctantly and very belatedly, responding to public pressure. As the family businesses that constitute local horticulture quietly disappear, the supermarkets that have presided over their demise are announcing their desire to buy locally. Well, they are too late. The farms, skills and infrastructure that go with local production have gone, leaving only pony paddocks and wheat fields. After three decades of being kicked, screwed and twisted, it will take more than the Tesco policy initiative to get growers to pick up their hoes again.

posh nosh to choke on

An organic estate is in danger of becoming the latest must-have for the very rich trying to give some meaning to their wealth. It is certainly a more laudable way of spending a fortune than gambling or collecting sports cars, but the accompanying air of Victorian philanthropy can be irksome to practitioners who have acquired their acres the hard way. There is also a tendency to want to create an exclusive brand to go with it.

During a recent tour around a large organic Cotswold estate, the brand manager boasted of how expensive their organic fillet steak was (fifty pounds per kilo). Not how good it was or how happy the cow had been or even the environmental richness of the estate where it had grazed. The pinnacle of his achievement was the divisive exclusivity of the brand. For him, organic was a niche, a market opportunity, a means of differentiation, a unique selling point, or any of the other ridiculous corruptions of the English language that smooth-tongued marketeers use to ply their oily trade.

I grew up in a large family where several of the farm workers would join us every day for the fantastic and plentiful lunches that my mother created. Eating is something we all do – a common denominator, an opportunity to bring people together and break down barriers. Organic farming should be an extension of this process because it is more respectful of food and the processes required to get it to the table. But the table must be accessible to everyone for it to be relevant.

Yes, organic should mean quality, provenance and animal welfare, but the organic I aspire to is also affordable, enjoyable and accessible with as little fuss as possible, regardless of people's income and background. You don't have to be posh or rich to enjoy your food. I feel at best ambivalent and often resentful of the exclusivity and divisiveness that the organic tag has acquired from some of the brands that have sprung up around it. Britain is a class-ridden society where people increasingly define themselves by what they eat. The founders of the organic movement were an earthy, practical lot with mud on their boots and a passion for the health of the soil and their livestock, and consequently that of the nation. I imagine they would be horrified by the exclusivity of brands such as Daylesford and Whole Foods and suspect they would be more at home in a Spud-u-like. To use exclusivity as a marketing tool is a betrayal of the essential inclusiveness and sharing at the heart of true organic farming.

supermarkets: a lifetime of loathing

My loathing for supermarkets was born almost twenty years ago, when I was making my first tentative approaches as a would-be supplier to Safeway (now consumed by Morrisons). The buyer asked me to come to London the following Thursday to meet his technologist colleague. When I asked if we could make it Friday, because I would be in London for the weekend, the phone went dead. I called back – "I'm sorry, I think we were cut off" – and was met with the buyer's immortal words: "No, sonny, when we whistle, you jump." I was new to the game and had not yet been beaten into the subservience that views this as normal behaviour. I went back to selling wholesale.

Supermarkets regard it as normal practice to demand promotional prices well below the cost of production. Suppliers are often expected to pay to get their products on the shelves and may be required to contribute to marketing campaigns and promotions outside their control. I was once asked to pay £1,000 to talk to a consultant who would advise me how to talk to Sainsbury's. Does it sound like dealing with the Mafia? It is; everyone knows it is wrong but they are powerless to change it. A few years later I met that Safeway buyer, who was now working for an organic packing company supplying the supermarkets, and found that he was not a demon but pretty decent. He had simply been doing what was expected within the environment he found himself in.

In my experience, supermarkets – with the exception of Waitrose and the Co-op, who are not stock-market-listed and so don't constantly worry about their share price – demean human behaviour and are almost universally loathed by their suppliers. Supermarket buyers make second-hand car salesmen seem like priests, but even they cannot maintain such unscrupulous unpleasantness with people they actually get to know – they are moved frequently before they form relationships with suppliers that might tempt them to decency.

The food industry, and vegetable growing and packing in particular, is a battlefield ravaged by the ruthless buying policy of the big four: Tesco, Asda, Sainsbury's and Morrisons. The country is strewn with the collateral damage of abandoned packhouses, redundant staff and bankrupt growers. After thirty years of supermarkets lecturing us on supply chain rationalisation (chopping out all but the largest suppliers), category management (pushing their costs on to their suppliers) and the need for continuity of supply (global supply chains), the wind has temporarily changed. Local is in, and their advertisements are all about local, seasonal sourcing (though genuinely locally-sourced products in Tesco currently amount to less than 1 per cent of sales). The reality is that ever-larger, more concentrated suppliers are merging, buying and taking each other over in a miserable ongoing battle to avoid being struck out by a buyer's pen at the next 'supplier review'.

I don't know whether to rant, laugh or throw up when the invitation arrives to a local suppliers' seminar organised by Tesco to reinvent the industry they have spent three decades destroying. Let no one forget that the publicly quoted Big Four exist to deliver dividends and shareholder value, pure and simple. For 'corporate social responsibility', read 'brand management and risk reduction'. Their positions on local sourcing, GM* food, organic farming, biodegradable* packaging, climate change or any of the other issues used to grab headlines are like autumn leaves, blown around by public opinion before being left to rot when the fickle wind of PR moves on. Their proclamations of green credentials and concern for public health leave me, for one, reaching for a bucket.

enough

See the happy moron, He doesn't give a damn. I wish I were a moron.
My God! Perhaps I am! Anonymous

Most of us live our lives the way my overweight Labrador eats
her dinner: in a frantic rush, with little pause for consideration
or appreciation and an almost paranoid resistance to sharing.
She salivates at any suggestion of food and invariably wants more
as soon as it is finished. For her, there is no such thing as enough.
It is said that her breed lacks the satiated gene and, given the
chance, would eat to obesity and ultimately death. I watch her
eat with pity. Like Pooh Bear, she is a dog of very little brain, but
her appetites are fairly harmless and, between meals, provided
there is no hint of a bin to raid or a child's lunch to steal, she is
loyal and endearingly happy in her skin.

I like to believe that I am smarter than my dog and, though
I admire her ability to live in the moment, as a higher being I
have the future to think about. Surely we should be able to organise
and live our lives for long-term happiness and fulfilment. Surely
we should be able to balance the fleeting pleasures of short-term
material gratification with the needs of our long-suffering planet.
All the evidence shows that material wealth in developed countries
is very poor at delivering lasting happiness, but we allow our
appetite for it to outweigh all the wisdom that would recommend
a more balanced life. I sometimes think we might stand a chance
of attaining that wisdom if it weren't for the fiendishly clever and
well-resourced marketing industry that is so adept at appealing
to our base desires.

JUNE 2018

"so how does it feel?"

I've been asked that question more than a few times in the
three weeks since we became employee owned. The answer?
I am starting to feel the soil under my feet again, my shoulders
definitely feel lighter, and an unfamiliar smile keeps settling on
my face. Maybe I'm imagining it, but I think my fellow co-owners
are smiling more too, and everyone's energy has gone up a gear.

I knew it was the right choice on the day: when we had the
best party the farm has ever seen, full of spontaneity and joy;
when my staff gave me a seat fashioned from the remains of last
winter's fallen oak; when we all signed a giant scroll as witnesses
to the occasion; when several staff, old and new, spoke movingly
of what Riverford means to them and their hopes for our future,
to rapturous applause; when I found myself standing on the
shoulders of two acrobats with a rose in my teeth... but most
of all when I staggered off, inebriated and overwhelmed, to take
a few minutes on my own and enjoy dusk falling into the valley.
For years I have loved that view, across the fields that I have
walked, planted, and hoed so many times – over the reservoir
where my children learnt to swim, to the wood-shrouded Tor
Hill. After a few moments, I saw that I was not alone: four equally
inebriated, previously landless co-owners were also taking in the
landscape. I shook myself when I realised it was no longer mine
– to do with as I pleased, to share if I wanted, or not if I didn't.

Now it was ours, forever, with no going back. To my surprise
and relief, in the last light of a perfect day, that felt perfect – and
it still feels perfect three weeks later.

My smile stems from the conviction that together we have taken action and made a small change. I often return to this quote from Chomsky: "If you assume that there is no hope, you guarantee that there will be no hope. If you assume that there is an instinct for freedom, that there are opportunities to change things, then there is a possibility that you can contribute to making a better world." To have sown a seed of hope and made a step towards the world I want to live in seems a very good reason to smile. So... it feels good. Some rain would make it even better.

LEXICON

Anaerobic fermentation

– fermentation without oxygen. Involved in sauerkraut, silage and kimchi making, but also in the foul-smelling activity of airless soil or mud.

The Archers

– BBC Radio Four's (and the world's) longest-running rural radio soap. Started in 1951 as a way of disseminating improved agricultural practice.

Biodegradable

– able to be digested/broken down by living organisms. Beware that, in theory, a nappy can be described as biodegradable, even though this might take a hundred years.

Biodynamic

– organic plus, including planting and harvesting by phases of the moon, using various natural concoctions, and burying cows' horns packed with cow manure over winter. Too mystic for me but some very good farmers swear by it.

Biotech(nology)

– the use of organisms to make stuff . . . so could be said to include farming, brewing, baking. More recently the term is commonly used with reference to genetic engineering and modification.

Calabrese summer broccoli

– the green uniform broccoli, originally from Calabria, Italy, as opposed to our hardier, local stuff.

Chitting

– waking tubers up in spring to sprout roots and shoots. For seed potatoes it's done in shallow trays in the light to encourage strong, short sprouts.

Clamp

– the traditional root store. A big pile, often covered with straw and/or soil, with varying levels of sophistication in its ventilation. Mimics the conditions in the soil, but with greater frost protection.

Conventional versus organic farming

– a bad and confusing distinction between those who fight nature with chemicals and those who try to work with it.

Curds

– the head of a cauliflower; actually a swollen meristem (growing point).

Flea beetle

– nasty, hard-to-kill jumping insects that plague (mainly) the cabbage family. They appear from nowhere to devour emerging brassica seedlings, particularly in hot, dry weather.

Fleeces – super light, spun polypropylene covers that warm and protect crops from insects.

'Gaia hypothesis' – James Lovelock's idea that the world's life forms and lifeless forms together would regulate our planet and maintain the conditions for life ... at least until we burned all that fossil fuel.

GM/Genetic modification – could be used to describe any breeding technique, but usually used to describe introducing a gene from one species to another. Exciting or scary, depending on your point of view.

Grader – a machine that sorts the big from the small; the thin from the fat; the yellow from the green; stones from potatoes.

Horsegate – when the murky meat trade was exposed in 2013 and it turned out many supermarkets and restaurants had no idea where or which animal their "beef" came from.

Inter-row weeding – hoeing, flaming or brushing to kill the weeds between rows of crops.

Loams – the soils we all want. A balanced mixture of sand, clay and organic matter.

Martin Bell – the man in a linen suit who stood as an independent MP in 1997 and ousted the sleazy Neil Hamilton . . . not sure what that has to do with vegetables.

Monsanto – they started with saccharine and moved on to DDT, Agent Orange, PCBs, bovine growth hormone and now GM crops. Given their track record of patenting, lobbying, exploiting and running away from the consequences when it goes wrong, their global power in the seed trade is truly scary.

Mycorrhiza – our hidden, neglected, misunderstood and often abused but vital fungal friends whose hyphae surround and penetrate plant roots and help them access nutrients, especially in poor soils.

Mycotoxin – toxins produced by fungus.

Natural England – government environmental advisors and grant-givers; they send us forms which we fill in, or more often pay consultants to fill in.

Nematodes – round worms. They are everywhere; some good (for us) and some bad. About 50% are parasitic but some of them are great at controlling pests like slugs and cutworms. Some plant-borne nematodes can devastate vegetable crops, particularly potatoes. They can be controlled by crop rotation and growing antagonistic plants such as mustard and marigolds.

Open pollinated – varieties that have been developed through random cross breeding and selecting desirable traits; crucially home-saved seed will breed true, allowing farmers and gardeners to keep their own seed and undertake local breeding to suit local conditions, in contrast to F1 hybrids which require the farmer to buy new seed, normally from the main global seed companies, every year.

Parthenogenesis – reproduction without sex. Pretty miserable, and for better or worse the children are all the same.

Pathogens – the bacteria, fungi and viruses that cause disease.

The Pig Idea – a campaign founded by Tristram Stuart and Thomasina Miers to reintroduce the practice of feeding kitchen waste to pigs and thereby restore their place as farm recyclers.

Silage – sauerkraut for cows. Grass that is pickled in the lactic acid produced when fermented without oxygen.

Soil Association – founded in 1947 by farmers, nutritionists and scientists who believed that healthy soil leads to healthy animals and healthy people. Today it certifies 80% of the organic produce in the UK. Sometimes contentious, and viewed by some as cranky, extreme or luddite, but I think they get most things right.

South Devon Organic Producers Cooperative – the achievement I am proudest of in my career; an insanely ambitious project that worked against all odds. Founded in 1997 by ten neighbouring Devon farmers. Supplies much of the veg for Riverford's Devon-packed boxes.

Stale seed beds – created by repeated shallow cultivations to germinate and then kill weed seeds near the soil surface, thereby reducing the soil weed "seed bank" and making weed control easier in subsequent crops.

Thermal weeding – killing weeds with a flamethrower. The organic answer to glyphosate, but less toxic (also less effective).

Tropism – the ability of plants to respond to their environment, e.g. growth towards light, upwards, downwards, towards nutrients etc.

Whey – the liquid by-product left after the removal of curds to make cheese. Used to be fed to pigs.

Wireworms – reddish, thin, soil-living larvae of click beetles which feed on many (particularly root) crops leaving stunted crops and/or hole-ridden roots. Most common after more than two years of grass.

WOMAD – World of Music, Arts and Dance festival, founded by Peter Gabriel in 1980. Great music; fewer drugs and cleaner toilets than most festivals and an almost weird absence of litter.

Worm casts – worm faeces pushed out onto the surface. A wonderful, intimate, bowel-ground mixture of mineral soil, organic matter and mucus. Great for building soil structure. Charles Darwin and organic farmers love them. Lawn lovers and golf-course keepers spend their lives trying to get rid of them.

ACKNOWLEDGEMENTS

There are too many save-the-world books and most of them are too long. This one is short, and, I hope, easy to read; even so it took some persuading and cajoling to get it over the line.

Thanks go to:

Rachel Lovell for her persistent enthusiasm.

Emma and Alex of Smith & Gilmour for their elegant design, and their unstinting support and advice which went way beyond the call of duty.

Our cartoon duo, Joe Berger and Pascal Wyse, for their wit and inventiveness.

My sister, Rachel Watson, for her faith in the project, her balance and wisdom.

My nieces, Anna Neima and Martha Sanderson, for their selection and editing, along with the various people at Riverford who have edited and questioned the weekly newsletters over the last quarter century.

The rest of my siblings for putting up with me when I have overstepped the mark or used "we" too liberally.

My father, John Watson, who encouraged me to aspire to be useful, to question everything, to do it my way, and to have an enduring faith in people.

1951
John Watson, Guy's father, rented Riverford, with 20 Ayrshire cows, lots of ideals, and no experience.

1968
A pig for his 8th birthday started Guy's farming career.

1970
Reading Rachel Carson's *Silent Spring* started John Watson's environmental awakening.

1986
Guy came home to grow his first 3 acres of veg.

1988
Globe artichokes, encountered in Britanny, started Guy's first veg love affair. He sailed the root stock home and landed them in a Devon cove.

1991
A fall out with a supermarket buyer set Guy on the way to veg boxes and independence.

1997
Growth led Guy to found a coop of local family farms.

1996
The year of black kale, before it became fashionable as cavolo nero.

1995
Early champion of purple sprouting broccoli – against the invasion of the foreign Calabrese.

1994
Red russian kale, spotted on a Spanish roundabout, became part of our growing year.

1993
Guy delivered his first veg boxes from an old Citroen 2CV to local 'box organisers'.

1992
Wet garlic, spotted in a Spanish market, became Guy's next growing experiment.

1998
Brother, Oliver, set up Riverford Organic Dairy to process unhomogenised milk from his herd.

1998
Guy discovers the nutty virtues of romanesco, its form reminding him of Madonna's Boadicea phase.

1998
Guy challenged in the High Court the use of Monsanto's GM by a neighbouring trial farm.

2004
A 'fat finger' moment on the calculator produced a radicchio crop ten times that planned: a chance to convert the nation to bitter leaves.